# MY BLUE COUNTRY

## O.R. MELLING

VIKING

VIKING
Published by the Penguin Group
Penguin Books Canada Ltd, 10 Alcorn Avenue, Toronto, Ontario, Canada
M4V 3B2
Penguin Books Ltd, 27 Wrights Lane, London W8 5TZ, England
Viking Penguin, a division of Penguin Books USA Inc., 375 Hudson Street,
New York, New York 10014, U.S.A.
Penguin Books Australia Ltd, Ringwood, Victoria, Australia
Penguin Books (NZ) Ltd, 182–190 Wairau Road, Auckland 10, New Zealand

Penguin Books Ltd, Registered Offices: Harmondsworth, Middlesex, England

First published 1996
10 9 8 7 6 5 4 3 2 1

Printed and bound in Canada on acid free paper ∞

**Canadian Cataloguing in Publication Data**

Melling, O.R.
  My blue country

ISBN 0-670-86642-3

I. Title.

PS8576.E463M9 1996      jC813'.54      C95-931347-8

Excerpts from the following used by permission:
"Mon Pays" by Gilles Vigneault. Copyright © Les Editions du Vent qui Vire (en
français)
From "Mon Pays Bleu" by Pierre Cour—French lyric of "Durham Town (The
Leavin') words & music by Roger Whittaker © controlled in USA & Canada by
Croma Music Company—130 W 57 St, NY NY 10019. Lyrics reproduced by
permission Tembo Music Ltd/BMG Music Publishing Ltd.

*For my dad, Kevin Whelan, 1921–1995,*
*now playing the bass Elsewhere.*

# Acknowledgments

*With special thanks to Wendy Baker,*
*my best bud in Malaysia and now the Yukon,*
*whose journals brought back the memories.*

*Thanks also to Benny Quay, for his kind assistance*
*with Bahasa Malaysia; Sajidah, Magella and Dr. Riaz*
*for re-introducing me to Islam in Co. Galway;*
*Senator Jacques Hébert for his encouragement and support; my*
*mom, Georgina Whelan, for babysitting and everything else; Frank*
*Golden for friendship and writerly support;*
*my editor Meg Masters and all at Penguin; and of course, Mick*
*Cullen, who arrived out of the blue and into my life.*

*The author also gratefully acknowledges a bursary from*
*the Arts Council of Ireland, granted to write this book.*

# Author's Note

*While the book draws on my experiences as a participant
of Canada World Youth/Jeunesse Canada Monde
in its first year, 1972–1973, this is a work of fiction.
The programme itself is not depicted as it was then
or as it exists now. As writers will do, I have changed
and created much to suit the purposes of my story.
All characters are fictional and any resemblance to
persons living or dead is entirely coincidental.*

Interview (yikes!)
Ottawa
September 4/1972
10:30 a.m.

## ARE YOU ADVENTUROUS?

Participants wanted for cross-cultural work project in the country of Malaysia, including the state of Sarawak in Borneo. Be prepared to open your minds and hearts to this once-in-a-lifetime opportunity to cross the East/West divide.

Ages 16-20.

Contact the appropriate Regional Office below

Got it!
I'm on my way
Yahoo!!

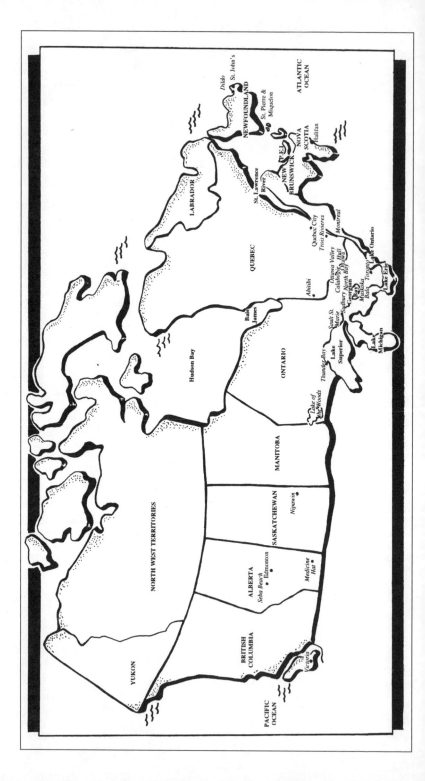

# PART ONE: CANADA

*"You finally get up the nerve to
take out the contents of your knapsack
and you discover that everyone has
the same stuff in theirs."*

J.C. McKinnock

October 2, 1972
Camp Pineridge, Muskoka, Ontario

*I*'ve promised myself I'm going to write in here every day to keep a record of this great adventure I've embarked upon. I should have started my journal the day of the interview in Ottawa but I was so sure I'd blown it when I admitted that I knew nothing about the project, CUSO (Canadian University Students Overseas), or any of the other youth programmes they were talking about. Like, hey, I'm really happy the government's into educating young people, but who hears about these things in Calabogie?! I must have got points for honesty, though, because here I am.

The day didn't start out so well. I got soaked in Toronto, lugging around my bulging suitcase (Mom!) plus winter coat and knapsack. I arrived an hour earlier than the meeting time and got bored hanging around the bus station so I headed off to gawk at the Big Apple. Sure beats home for things to look at. I prefer the old city hall to the new one. The old one looks like a Gothic lunatic asylum but the new one's like a reject from a Tupperware party. Stuffed myself with five (!) greasy egg rolls from a Chinese take-out. The traffic, the noise and the crowded sidewalks soon tired me out (read: felt a bit lost and lonely) so I went back to the station.

There were so many kids with knapsacks, I couldn't figure out who was part of the project and who wasn't. Went upstairs and found a "welcome/bienvenue" sign with our logo on it. People were arriving in dribs and drabs, from the airport and the train station, by bus and by car, from every part of Canada. As more and more gathered, you could feel the excitement in the air. Something special was happening and I was part of it!

The first person to talk to me was Lise Montaigne, from Quebec, a small pretty woman with long hair. She checked my name off a list and asked me a few questions—was the bus trip okay, was I nervous, etc. Very friendly, she made me feel I belonged. At first I thought she and Val Trypuc, the project co-ordinator, were married but they're not. He's single, she's a group leader.

When we were all accounted for, we looked like a huge mob. Sixty-eight of us, including the group leaders and Mr. Trypuc, I mean, Val. He hates being called "mister." Makes him feel old and respectable, he said, ha ha. He is an old guy, in his forties I think, and looks like a schoolteacher. Kind of paunchy and homely looking, wears glasses, and is going bald on top. The kind of person you know you can go to with your problems (not that I'm planning to have any).

We were packed onto a bus to take us north to our first training camp. Everyone was shy and quiet as the bus moved out of the city and left the suburbs behind. I let out a sigh as Ontario farmland spread out on either side of the highway like wings. The fields were brown or dark green, wet and cold in the rain, but they looked familiar, like the Ottawa Valley. Staring out the window, Greyhound-bound, I told myself I was travelling towards unknown territory, to a future of unimaginable experiences.

Val, our co-ordinator, got things going by making us stand up, one by one, to say our names, ages and where we came from, plus a few sentences about our lives. Centre-

4

shot or what. Everyone looked awkward as they spoke, but it broke the ice and we felt free to talk to each other after that. Some of the kids have travelled quite a lot, but most are like me—from a small town, just finished high school, summer jobs the only real experience. I was surprised when the French kids spoke in their own language. I mean, it never occurred to me they would be on the project. Great—I'll get to practise *la langue*!

I like this place, Pineridge. It brings back memories of summer camp. We're in log cabins inside a forest. You step outside into the smell of pine, the forest floor covered in cones, and branches of evergreen overhead. There's a lake just beyond the ridge, bordered by hills and more forest. In a clearing by the road is the main lodge containing the kitchen, showers and dining hall.

The cabins smell of pine wood and have bunks in them but nothing else. Good thing we were told to bring sleeping bags. I'm sitting on a top bunk writing this while the other girls are talking, unpacking or getting their stuff ready to go out and wash. There's a washing area not far from the cabin, metal sinks with cold-water taps and a roof over it but no walls. Too rough for me. I put toothpaste on my teeth and brushed them clean. I'll take a shower in the main lodge tomorrow. Some of the kids are already complaining about the facilities. Gawd, we just got here. How do they think they are going to make it in Malaysia? Who knows what the facilities will be like there?

All the girls in my cabin seem really nice. Too nice? It's too early to really know anybody. Everyone's on their best behaviour because we're all strangers. Wait till the zits start showing, ha ha.

I'm too tired to write any more. Meeting 67 people in one day is a major strain on the brain.


October 11, 1972

So much for my plans to make this a daily diary. But the days are so full and then we spend the nights talking till all hours, I don't have much time to myself.

The first day we had a general meeting. Each of the group leaders stood up and read out a list of who was in their group. They divided everyone up by male/female and French/English, but we are free to change around over the coming weeks. This is to "kick-start the process" as Val explained. Lise Montaigne is my group leader! I'm so happy since I liked her from the start.

I'm using my French a lot, far out, especially with the two girls in my cabin who have hardly any English. Claire's from Abitibi in Quebec and Louise, who's in my group, is from Saskatchewan. She's Métis. There have been clashes between the English and French kids and the general meeting last night turned into a major shouting match. The English are being insensitive, talking too fast and making noise when French is being spoken. *Tout le monde achète des dictionnaires.* The French kids ARE HERE and we've got to speak their language.

Next week we start Malay lessons when the Malaysian co-ordinators arrive. There will also be jobs to do, insulating the cabins and cleaning up the camp, but that hasn't started yet. Things are pretty loose at the moment as everyone settles in.

Today I went canoeing with Betty, the group leader from British Columbia. She belongs to the Haida tribe and she taught me how to say "lake," "canoe" and "sky." I kept repeating the words so I wouldn't forget and they echoed over the surface of the water—*súu, tlúu, ya'an ka'an*—like the cry of a loon. The red canoe was light and fast. I knelt in the bow, Betty steered from behind. Above us, the sky was a deep blue and around us, the hills were covered in trees changing their colours. All those Group of Seven paintings rolled into one! Afterwards we had a quick dip though the water was ice-cold and then we lounged on the wooden dock to admire the scenery. Betty said she didn't know that Ontario was so like her own province. She always thought of Eastern Canada (what the Westerners call Ontario, can you believe it?!) as being another country altogether.

Though it's warm enough to swim, fall is definitely here. There's a nip in the wind that says a new season has arrived. It makes me feel alive and excited. *Change* is in the air. You can smell it. You can breathe it in. Anything can happen. Everything is possible.

October 14, 1972

*I* have to write this out as I feel so rotten. This project is hard-going sometimes. It isn't easy dealing with group stuff and all the differences between everybody. Somehow we've got to join together or we'll never be ready for Malaysia. I mean, I know that's the point of the training camps—to get us living and working together, to prepare us for the same kind of situation overseas—but is it possible that the whole thing could fail? That we'll just fall apart and collapse under the strain? It's never been done before. This is the first year of the project, the test pilot really, and if it doesn't succeed there won't be another one. Hey—give me the world to carry on my back.

The general meetings are becoming one big hassle after another, though the French/English thing is sorting itself out. Both the English and the French kids are using their second language more. But there are a lot of complaints about the food. Each group takes their turn cooking in the kitchen. Most times it's puke-city. And also the facilities. Sometimes you have to wait up to an hour to get a shower. Boredom is setting in and a lot of kids head into Bala to drink beer all day in the hotel. The work projects aren't well organized and hardly anybody works. There are no rules, you work if you want to, so guess what. Nobody works.

The pressure is on to form final groups. There are lots of "floaters" who haven't made up their minds yet. They wander in and out of groups, joining and then leaving again. That makes everything shaky and unstable. As one of the guys said in the *grande réunion* last night "trying to get a grip on this project is like nailing jelly to a tree."

Couples are forming fast. Never mind cross-culturalism, cross-pollination is the name of the game. I hate that. It makes me feel left out.

The one good thing that happened this week—the whole camp went co-ed! For an experiment. For the experience. Guys and girls sleeping in the same cabins. I thought it would be embarrassing, but everyone's being sensitive about not looking when people are dressing and undressing. And it's fun talking late at night with guys in the room. They tell all too! They say they don't talk that way with just guys around but they find it easier if girls are there.

The guys in our cabin wanted the low-down on menstruation. I nearly died, but Helen from Halifax and Isabelle from Hull got right into it. They did a bilingual show-and-tell with different kinds of tampons and sanitary pads with glasses of water. The guys talked about wet dreams and how, when it first happened and they woke up soaking wet, they thought they had something wrong with them and they were going to die. That's exactly how I felt when I got my first period! Funny though, when you talk about stuff like that in a relaxed atmosphere it doesn't feel like a Big Dark Secret or something to be ashamed of.

We've been getting needles all week and there's more to come, for cholera, yellow fever, typhoid, smallpox, polio and tetanus. One of the big shots was called gamma globulin and it was murder. I had to lie down for the afternoon. They told us we'll have to take malaria tablets all the time we're in Malaysia. Yikes.

I have to stop writing. Everyone's talking about their most embarrassing moments and it's too good to miss. I feel better now that I've got everything off my chest. "Where there's life there's hope," as my gran always says.

October 20, 1972

Got a phone call from Mom today, in Val's office. Dad had another attack and is in the hospital. I feel like dropping this whole thing and racing home but Mom said no, he's going to be alright and I'll see them at Christmas. She was trying to sound as if everything was fine but I know that voice she uses when she's pretending. Matt and Daniel are with her, but still, I should be too. I feel so guilty that I never called, but there's always a long line-up for the pay phone. Actually, the truth is I haven't even thought of home since I got here. I've been so busy and it's just so great to be free and independent. (How can I say that with Dad ill!) Wrote Mom a long letter and sent Dad a home-made get-well card with all my love.

There's been some major stealing going on in the camp. Everyone is being more careful with their things. We had a meeting about it after lunch yesterday. Some kids are obviously a lot poorer than others. Maybe they figure they're balancing the situation? But can we know *why* if we don't know *who?* There was a big discussion about "class" and I was surprised when Bob from Sudbury said I was middle class. His dad's a miner. I argued with him because I don't agree. My dad has a grocery store but, as he always says, it's owned by the bank not us. Gramps was a small farmer who lost everything during the Depression. We have a nice house but it isn't like the doctor's or anything. But then, my parents do send me pocket-money to add to the dollar a day we get on the project. Other kids live on that amount. I never thought about what class I might be in or that there were poor people in Canada. Bob says that's a sure sign I'm "bourgeois"! He lent me a book, *The Poverty Wall* by Ian Adams. I was up all last night reading it. It blew my mind. I thought Canadians were either rich or like us, "scraping by," as Mom describes it. I didn't know there was real poverty in Canada.

I'm learning so much here that I would never have discovered at home. One kid has hardly any clothes so I offered her my best T-shirt. She was insulted and got really angry. What an idiot I was. I apologized to her and explained that it wasn't charity, I was trying to "redistribute wealth" as Bob would say. I guess she understood because she accepted my apology and asked for the T-shirt back.

## October 24, 1972

*T*he visit from the Ottawa bigwigs has taken its toll. We've got Rules. Policies sent from Head Office in Montreal. No more leaving camp. Kids were hitching to Orillia, Gravenhurst and Huntsville to spend the day drinking or shopping. Some would disappear for weekends, even four or five days at a stretch. So now you're either on the project or *out*. Work has to be organized and take place at least half a day every day, Monday to Friday. No more co-ed!!! There was a big rebellion over that one. Politics are involved. The federal government, who funds us, doesn't want any bad publicity with the election coming up. Kids living together is not cool. Some of the kids agreed to stop till after the election, but others refused and their cabins are still co-ed despite the rule. Mine isn't though, and I'm sad about that. I miss the guys already. I mean, all we were doing was talking. Do they really think people are going to mess around with everyone else in the room? Gross. Katie Daly from Newfoundland, who's in my group, stood up at the meeting and started yelling.

"Why should we worry about the fucking government?

Let them fall."

Val smiled before answering her. (He likes Katie, you can tell.)

"Fair enough, Katie, but if the government falls so do we. The Conservatives don't back this kind of programme, you know that."

And if things weren't bad enough at the project level, my group is driving me crazy. All we ever do is fight. I can't stand it any more. I'm considering changing groups... No, I won't. I've got to make this work. So much of this stuff is about *not quitting*. Hanging in through thick and thin.

But why can't we get along with our group leader? If we're not fighting among ourselves we're all fighting with her. She says we're rebelling against a female authority figure, the girls as well as the guys. Hmm. Something to think about. My dad's always been the boss in our family, Mom even calls him "The Boss" and he always has the last say on everything. Mom is a strong person in her own right, has to be with three kids, the store and the garden, plus looking after Gran who's an invalid, but she's the kind of silently strong person who stays in the background. Lise is totally different. Takes command, is very aggressive, doesn't back down easily. Maybe she's right. Maybe if she was a man we wouldn't find it so difficult to accept her as she is. Maybe we'd just think of her as a good leader.

I'll do a recap of my group. After a few changes, drop-outs and drop-ins, it looks like this is the gang I'm going to Malaysia with (Lord give me strength):

LISE MONTAIGNE: Québecoise from Trois-Rivières, totally bilingual, used to teach emotionally disturbed kids. (She should be more patient with us with that kind of experience.) Small-boned, very pretty, long dark-brown hair to her waist. Doesn't look anywhere near 28, looks young like us. Talks fast, moves fast, a small bundle of energy. I want a copy of that poster she's got in her cabin: all these sheep are running towards a cliff and falling off and this voice bubble above them says "*Excusez-moi...excusez-moi*" and then you spot one little sheep inside the crowd, heading back in the other direction. Right on!

RAY BENNETT: Westerner, 17, from Edmonton, Alberta, very tall straggly guy, a "long drink of water" as Mom would say. Kind of cute in a little-boy way but that brushcut needs to be grown in, ugh. Bilingual and talks very fast in both French and English. Brains to burn. He intimidates me a bit, really smart people always do. I need to build up my confidence in that area.

KATIE DALY: Second-generation Irish, from St. John's, Newfoundland. Very small and skinny, undernourished looking, in fact looks like a kid of about 12 though she's 17. Mop of red curly hair plus freckles completes the Orphan Annie image. She's very brainy too. She and Ray are always trying to outdo each other in discussions. Both of them are extremely competitive. Not my kind of people, but I can take them in small doses. Katie's not bilingual (Ray has her there). She sure can drink for a tiny person. Goes into a rage if anyone tells Newfie jokes. Another lesson for me, I thought they were harmless!

LOUISE BOISVERT: Métis from Nipawan, Saskatchewan. She's 18 but seems older as she acts mature. The first to become part of a couple (with Claude, see below). Plays guitar and sings like a nightingale. Her English isn't great and gets worse when she's angry or excited, but because she's so extroverted she keeps going anyway. (Must be more confident with my French. It's being self-conscious about it that makes you dry up and get tongue-tied.) Louise wears dresses, not jeans, usually skirts and blouses. Old-fashioned and very feminine. Gran would love her.

CLAUDE LACASSE: 21, the oldest on the project. The limit was 20, but he was the right age when he applied, lucky for us. He's training to be a chef and the whole camp cheers when it's our turn in the kitchen. Claude makes up the menu and puts the rest of us to work, chopping vegetables, stirring sauces, etc. and the meals are fantastic. He's from Quebec City, very dark and handsome. Speaks very little English, but I think he's a quiet guy anyway. I always feel safe when he's around, he's so calm. He's the one who usually stops the fights in our group. Ray, Katie, Lise and the next guy are the ones who are the cause of them.

14

DARREN HELLIWELL: 18, WASP from Rosedale in
Toronto. Upper middle class—even I recognized
that—really wealthy, his dad's an international
banker. Extremely cute, blond, blue-eyed, strong
jaw. Tall, too. The kid who has everything. Went
to Upper Canada College. He's pretty smart,
though he's hopeless at French and I mean totally.
Talks like a wooden duck. He can be very funny
but sometimes his remarks are superior and
sarcastic. Likes to play "Lord of the Manor"
(Katie's phrase).

CYNTHIA GOODMAN: 18, Jewish Quebecker from
Westmount in Montreal. Bilingual. Here we are
talking classical beauty. Dark curls of hair to her
shoulders, amazing eyes, clear skin, slender figure.
Makes me green with envy. She and Darren would
make a gorgeous couple if they didn't hate each
other. Cynthia doesn't say it out loud but I can see
it in her eyes when she glares at him. Darren told
a Jewish princess joke in one of our meetings
(I am beginning to realize that some "jokes" are
not funny at all). Cynthia went stiff and silent but
Katie lost it and called him "a typical English bigot
with the sensitivity of a cockroach." She's got the
Irish way with words. That was one of the fights in
our group. I think Katie's a bit much for Cynthia
too, though, because she (Katie) is so proud of
being working class and makes a big deal of it and
Cynthia is obviously quite rich. Like Darren she
went to a private school.

I should do me too. Group photo.

JESSICA CATHERINE McKINNOCK, call me Jesse: 17
(just turned it this month). Scottish descent, from
the 1800s mind you, but Dad's still proud of it.
Good face, shame about the body. Best feature,
thick auburn hair to my waist. Not bilingual, but
plugging away at it. Small-town girl in every sense
of the word but out to learn about the world. Let
me at it! Favourite pastimes: reading and writing.
Crabby in the morning but otherwise a cheerful
sort. Hmm. Big boobs (second-best feature).
Gawd, it's so much easier to write about other
people than yourself. So much easier to see them
in one glance. Well, if I learn nothing else from
this project, maybe I'll find out more about
myself. Maybe I'll discover who I really am!

I hope my dad's going to be okay. Please, God...

October 30, 1972

*T*hings have really changed around here. It's as if everyone decided together that it was time to stop goofing
off and get down to business. Just about everybody gets up
for work these days, kids waking up other kids to get them
moving. All around the camp you bump into work gangs in
blue jeans and lumberjack shirts heading off through the
trees with picks and shovels or climbing up ladders onto
roofs with hammers and nails. We've insulated all the cabins

and repaired a few that were damaged in a fire last year. Two of the groups are digging holes for septic tanks. It was fun learning basic carpentry from the camp workmen, but the girls had to fight to get the tools off the guys, they were so sure we couldn't use them. As if they'd ever done this work either. Men!

There's less social intermingling these days. Each group meets more often and does things together with their own members. My group is still fighting like cats and dogs, but I'm getting used to it, even join in now and then. If you can't beat them... We've got a real reputation, none of the last floaters come near us. *Les guerriers* they're calling us. But we're not as unpopular as the élite group, the *crème de la crème* (this is all sarcastic). That's Tony's group. They don't have meetings, they have "happenings." Massage each other, sit around and play guitar, burn incense and hug each other. They don't join the work teams which is what really pisses everybody off. Bunch of hippies. Hah, they'll have to clean up their act before Malaysia, since that country hates hippies.

We are preparing for Malaysia at last. We've watched several documentaries on it. What an incredibly beautiful country! It looks like paradise, the Garden of Eden. I can't wait to get there. The Malaysian co-ordinators, Maya and Azahar, finally arrived after all kinds of delays, and they've been giving us talks and language lessons. *Saya chakap Bahasa Malaysia sedikit.* Maya is an Indian woman (there are three main races in Malaysia: Indian, Malay and Chinese). She's a journalist, tall and slender, with short dark hair, very pretty. Sometimes she wears Western clothes and other times she wears beautiful saris made from shimmering materials of the most gorgeous colours. Azahar is Malay, a Youth Ministry official, one of the government men who set up the project in Malaysia, and very dedicated to it. He's married with four kids and he misses his family. At the introductory talks, he said that he was the kind of man who got homesick when he left his village, never mind his country, but he felt the project was worth the sacrifice. He said that what we were doing would contribute to world understanding and peace. Wow, that freaked everybody out, as I don't think any of us thought the project was really important, at least not to anyone else but ourselves. When Maya spoke, she agreed with Azahar and said that whenever people of different cultures met together with mutual respect, they shone a light on Earth to show the way. (My throat felt very tight at that.)

So suddenly we have a sense of purpose, like all the hassles and problems are minor details compared to the Big Idea that we are trying to represent. I think everyone is a bit different now, attempting to live up to the great expectations of the project. Sure we're still all driving each other nuts, but somehow that's not the central issue any more, not the heart of the matter. The heart of this project is something else. Something pure and shining.

*tarang*—shining

November 1, 1972

*B*ahasa Malaysia is quite easy to learn. The verb never changes for one thing, hurrah. You just put a word in front of it to make it past (*telah*), present (*sedang*) or future (*akan*). And it stays the same whether it goes with I (*saya*), you (*awak/kamu*), he/she (*dia*), we (*kami*) or they (*mereka*). I love the plurals. You say the word twice! *Tuan tuan* is men. *Puan puan* is women. *Belia belia* is youth. When you write it, you put a little 2 at the end of the word. *Tuan$_2$. Puan$_2$. Belia$_2$.*

*Apa khabar?*—How are you?

Actually I'm great, except a little tired. We had a Hallowe'en party last night. It was a hoot, everyone dressed up. I was Anne of Green Gables in my checkered dress with a white apron from the kitchen and my hair in braids. Ray is such a scream. He went as Pierre Berton with a spotted bow-tie and loads of Brylcreem. We danced a lot together, as "the two Canadians," ha ha. What a piss-up. Being Scots Presbyterian, needless to say I never saw so much booze in my life. Mom was afraid I might drink and gave me a lecture before I left. Since my brother Daniel drinks like a fish, she's resigned to the idea that we're not all going to follow the family tradition of teetotallers. I only had two beers though, so I didn't lose my senses like most people I know, and I got a good view of what was going on. Couples really form quickly when people drink. They start hanging off of each other and necking while they're dancing, and the next thing you know they're heading out the door.

They gave us a talk about drugs and alcohol in one of the early meetings. Val pointed out that he couldn't stop the older kids from drinking but that under-age drinking, as well as the use of dope, could undermine the project, even close it down. All that did, of course, was make everyone secretive. There's always some kind of dope being smoked in my cabin. The smell is pleasant but it gives me a headache. Since I don't smoke cigarettes I figure I'd choke to death if I tried it. Anyway I feel guilty enough about drinking, if I tried drugs I wouldn't be able to look Mom in the eye. I mean it was such a BIG DEAL when I started wearing make-up.

I found out something shocking tonight. Two kids are leaving the project! Just decided they didn't like it and are packing up to go home! I never even thought about the choice of quitting. I took it for granted that we were all committed to seeing things through. Val says we have to respect their decision and give them credit for knowing what's best for them, but I feel really angry and betrayed. They're rejecting everything we've been working so hard for, just like that!

I guess I'm angry because it makes me feel insecure. Like nothing is guaranteed. Maybe no matter how hard we work, or how hard we try, people will bail out, the whole thing could flounder, it could all go wrong. Is the project expecting too much? Are we all too young for this?

November 3, 1972

Went for a hike with Lise today, just her and me. The forest seemed to get darker and denser the further away we moved from camp. The ground crunched underfoot, matted with needles and dried twigs. We spent hours walking and talking, then sat down on a fallen tree trunk for a lunch of tuna sandwiches and hot coffee from a

Thermos. It was a great day. I can see why Lise is a group leader. I poured out all my doubts and worries and she listened to everything I said without arguing or interrupting. In fact she nodded her head at a lot of my points. Then she talked about the ideals of the project.

She said normally when the Western nations meet other countries we do it in a superior way, as if we know everything and they know nothing. But the project intends to meet the Malaysians not only as equals but with the understanding that *we will learn from them.* Lise said a youth project is the best way to do this because it's easier to work out new ideas with young people. We are less likely to think there's only one way to do something or one way to view life, and we are more open and able to learn and to change. She said all the hassles we're going through are "part of the process" and I have to give up my idea of anything being secure or guaranteed. That's what children need, but adult life isn't like that. Failure is as much a part of life as success and all of us will both fail and succeed throughout our lives.

"This project could fail," she said. "The organizers in Malaysia and Canada are aware of that. As you say, the whole thing could turn out to be a disaster. But that doesn't mean we shouldn't try, means even more so that we should, because the whole world is failing at this—different groups of people living in harmony together. It's only when we stop trying that all will be lost."

We talked about the French and English in Canada and the separatist movement in Quebec and the FLQ. A lot of her friends are separatists and she's not so sure she isn't one too, but she thinks that as long as people on both sides still want to make it work, then it's worth the effort.

21

Before I came on this project and met all the French kids, I never thought about Quebec leaving. It was all politics and wasn't real for me. Gawd, Lise is right. Nothing is guaranteed. Not even your own country!

It wasn't a reassuring talk now that I think about it. I wanted her to tell me everything was going to be fine. But somehow she made me feel stronger by facing the truth, made me realize I could accept the possibility of failure.

This project is really the most amazing thing I have ever done in my life.

## November 5, 1972

We were supposed to leave Pineridge today for our next training camp, but bad news. One of the kids, Mary from Victoria, contracted viral meningitis! She's in hospital. She's okay, but that's her out of the project and we're all quarantined for a week. Two pills four times a day. Everyone watching out for everyone else in case anyone gets headaches or sleeps too long. Doctors and nurses check us daily. The tension is incredible. Especially since we're all hanging around where we aren't supposed to be with no work projects and no leisure activities (read: Bala Hotel for beer). You'd think that would make things unbearable, with people cracking up and fighting, etc., but funny thing, it's having the opposite effect. Everyone is quieter, kind of gentle with each other, like we've all been shipwrecked and we have to pull together to survive. Even the general meetings are calm. Everyone's waiting...patiently waiting.

## November 9, 1972

*A*ll clear! Quarantine lifted. The news tore the lid off the place. It was like an explosion, everyone went berserk. There was a water fight after dinner when they made the announcement. It was dark outside, but the lights shone out the windows of the main lodge to light up all these crazies running around with buckets of water and hoses and jugs and bags and any kind of container, filling them with water and flinging them at everybody and anybody. Total chaos. It was like the end of the world when devils run through the streets (Gran). We were all screeching and hollering and nearly sick from laughing so much. Everybody got soaked. Neither Val nor the group leaders tried to stop us. Val was drenched and I mean *drenched*. He looked like a used tea bag. When things finally settled down, we had to clean up the mess but that was okay. We needed something to do since all of us have been packed and ready to go for the past week. We leave tomorrow for a camp in northern Alberta. Why are we moving? The group leaders say that Pineridge is basically a summer camp and won't be suitable in the winter months, but I think there's more to it than that. This whole training thing is about preparation. I think they want us to get used to travelling around together and adjusting to change as a group, since we'll be moving around Malaysia for different work projects.

I wonder how things will go in Alberta? I've already learned so much, what new stuff could possibly be in store for me? Sometimes I wish I could peek into the future to see what I'm doing there. After that talk with Lise, I realize how lonely I am even with all these people around. I wish I

23

had a boyfriend or better still a close girlfriend, someone my own age I could confide in. I guess it should be someone in my group since that's who I'm going to Malaysia with. Louise? Unlikely. Besides being part of a couple with Claude, she and Cynthia are best friends. That happened naturally I guess since both of them speak French and are more mature and ladylike. That leaves Katie. But she's so…I don't how to put this…*extreme*. Oh forget it. I can't know the future so I'll just have to go with the flow.

November 12, 1972
Camp Heart, Seba Beach, Alberta

*T*he train trip across Canada was a real experience. Traversing the country on the Canadian National, you get a true sense of how BIG this land is. Northern Ontario went on forever, a dark green trail of forests and gorges, a thousand shining lakes, Georgian Bay and Sault Ste. Marie, a northern spine of rock crowned with balsam, over the great hump of Lake Superior, outcrops of Douglas fir and tamarack, past Thunder Bay and Lake of the Woods. All my favourite Gordon Lightfoot songs were ringing in my head.

Then into the West. The prairies—wow! Hours and hours and miles and miles of golden brown plains as flat as an ocean, with grain elevators rising on the horizon like lighthouses. When we were crossing Saskatchewan, one of the guys, Trevor, shouted out, "That's our farm." Half an hour later someone asked whose land it was now and he said, "Still ours." We were all stunned. He doesn't act like a rich kid (read: Darren), but then he explained that you can't run a small farm on the prairies and his dad and all his uncles own a co-op.

I would never have guessed Trevor was a country boy. For one thing, his hair is down to his shoulders, so I took it for granted he was a city kid. (No one wears their hair long in Calabogie, guys that is.) When he left to join the project, the local band gave him a send-off at the train station, playing "For He's a Jolly Good Fellow." Neat. Our local newspaper printed a story about me and took a photo of me beside my suitcase. Mom and Gran were delirious.

For most of the trip everyone packed into the bar car as it was the only place we could gather together. Well, that's the excuse. The first night was wild. Katie started up a round of Maritimer songs and made everyone join in. That inspired Jean-François (from Betty's group, *un petit* cutie) to lead us singing French ones. They ended up taking turns and bowing to each other like maestros. *Farewell to Nova Scotia my sea-bound shore. V'la l'bon vent, v'la joli vent.* It was great fun. Everyone got drunk. I was tipsy on four beers but couldn't keep it up. (I'll never make an alcoholic like the rest of them, sigh.) By the time I left, Katie and Jean-François were necking in the corner, leaving everyone to sing their own songs.

The next morning I went into the dining car for first-call breakfast. Practically no one was up at that hour, hangover-city. I was eating on my own when Katie came in. I was surprised to see her up so early as she was always a late riser at camp. She looked very pale and bleary and, how can I describe it, kind of sheepish. She and I had never really spoken in a close way but as soon as she came into the car she looked *really* happy to see me. That surprised me but also made me feel good, like I could accept her a bit more.

"I'll just have coffee. Very black," she said to the waiter.

"The Eggs Benedict are terrific," I told her.

"I'd barf."

Manitoba was rattling past the window in the early sunshine, covered with a light snowfall and blinding white.

Katie hid her eyes with a groan. "I wish I had sunglasses." Then she peeped out at me. "Do I look any different?"

"A bit hung-over," I answered. That was being kind. She looked *très très* hung-over. Her red hair was in tangles like a bramble bush. She was as pale as the snow outside, with purple smudges under her eyes. "You could do with some sleep."

Then suddenly, I knew. I don't know how, but it was like telepathy, a blinding flash of inspiration. It was as if there was no one else on the train but her and me, no one else in the whole snowy winter of Canada except the two of us, hurtling through time and space. And I knew this was an incredibly important moment, not only in her personal history but in mine too. Because I was the first person she was about to tell. I can't say exactly how I felt, but it was like an honour.

"I lost it last night."

Wow! Even though she whispered it, even though I had guessed, it was like an explosion in my brain. For one thing, I had taken for granted that I was the only virgin on the project. That moment of truth from Katie—from someone I figured must have slept with loads of guys from the way she drinks and smokes and necks—made me see

the whole world differently. For some reason, I always figure I'm the odd one out, the one without the information
or the experience, the clueless one, the one who doesn't
know anything while everyone else knows everything.
Suddenly I realized we were all kids together and probably
most of us are virgins though pretending not to be and
putting on a big front.

And that was the moment when I decided I liked Katie.
She wasn't pretending to be an expert. She was being so
honest about it. She had no make-up on and that made her
look even younger, like a little kid who had stolen some
candy. She was waiting for me to say something, her face
nervous and pinched. I think she was afraid that I might
judge her or call her something bad. She was being so open,
it made me feel free to be honest too. (No masks, as Val
would say.)

"Far out," I said. "What's it like?"

Her features kind of collapsed with relief and she had a
big grin on her face.

"You too, eh? I thought I was the last of the Mohicans,
holding out at my age."

We both laughed.

It doesn't sound too good from her description. He got
on top of her and it hurt like hell, sharp stabbing pains
(omigod), but thankfully it didn't go on for too long. She
was drunk and so was Jean-François. (He didn't even know
and she didn't even tell him! Maybe he was a virgin too?)
There was blood on the sheets but she pretended she was
having her period. When Jean-François fell asleep, she lay
there wide awake and cried a bit because she felt lonely
even though he had his arm around her.

"It's supposed to get better, the more you do it," Katie said. She didn't look convinced.

I'm beginning to wonder if the whole thing isn't a Big Lie, like when they tell women it doesn't hurt to have a baby. (How could it not?!)

We talked for ages. Katie drank an entire pot of coffee and smoked cigarettes. I used her meal ticket to get another breakfast. It was all so exciting having this heart-to-heart talk about sex with someone who had just done it, I had to eat. She didn't mind me asking her a hundred questions. Like, wasn't she afraid of getting pregnant?

Nope. One of her older sisters put her on the Pill when she was sixteen. She, the older sister, got pregnant when she was that age and had to give up the baby. (How sad.)

I learned something else about Katie during that talk, a hilarious secret. When I said I would never have figured her for a virgin, coming from the big city and all, she looked at me blankly.

"St. John's is pretty big, isn't it?" I said.

"Bigger than where I come from," she replied with a shrug.

"But I thought, I mean, didn't you say you came from St. John's when we introduced ourselves on the bus?"

"You expect me to tell a bunch of strangers I comes from *Dildo*?"

We laughed so loud the waiter came running to see what was wrong.

By the time we were finished (Jean-François came look-ing for her) I felt I had truly made a friend. Katie even thanked me for being there and said she had hoped to find a friend on the project as she has so many girlfriends back home. So—hurrah! I've got a close friend at last and she's in my group. Maybe I'll find a boyfriend too? Hope burns eternal in the human heart (Mom).

After writing all that, I'm too tired to describe this place. Will try to make time tomorrow, though everything here is so much more organized than at Pineridge, you don't get a lot of free time.

*kawan*—friend

## November 13, 1972

*M* *on pays ce n'est pas un pays, c'est l'hiver!* We are in the heart of winter up here. The hills are covered in snow, the lake is frozen and the bare branches of the trees snap off like icicles. As far as the eye can see, the land is white. On our first day, my group trekked along the lakeshore, throwing snowballs at each other and making angels in the snow. The northern temperatures are sub-zero but it's a crisp dry cold and sometimes you hardly need a coat.

Camp Heart is fantastic. The cabins are more like chalets, each with a big bathroom that has loads of sinks and showers (heaven). There are several lodges with meeting rooms which have blackboards, plus recreational areas with shuffleboards, card tables, televisions and stereos! The dining room is huge, like a ballroom, airy and bright, with a kitchen staff. Hurrah we don't have to cook. There was an immediate rebellion among the girls when we heard that we were the only ones to work in the kitchen. "No males allowed." But the staff, all older women, folded their arms across their chests and said this was the way they ran their kitchen and that was that. The jobs are strictly divided: boys mop the floor, clear and wash tables and look after the garbage; girls help prepare meals and wash dishes. Big machine to do it, hurrah again!

Most of us accepted what they said (like we had much choice), though a few grumbled. Claude talked to "the ladies" as he calls them, told them he was studying to be a chef and asked if he might work with them since their kitchen was so professional. (His English is getting better, ha ha.) I guess they couldn't resist his charm because he's allowed in and they call him *Monsieur* and keep inviting him over to see what they're doing. What a hoot. Katie says they cluck around him like nuns around a priest. (She's R.C.)

No complaints about the food. Breakfast this morning was platters of French toast with jugs of maple syrup, freshly squeezed orange juice and real coffee. I pigged out completely.

No fooling around in this camp, let me tell you, it's all business and brass tacks. Four hours of physical work per day, strictly supervised by the camp's janitors; mending fences, digging a basement, painting cabins, washing windows, shingling roofs, clearing snow from the sidewalks and off the flat roofs. Darren shovelled a load of snow on top of me and Cynthia as we were walking by. We pelted him back with snowballs and nearly knocked him off the roof, ha ha. Some of the kids were grumbling in the general meeting that we're being used as cheap labour, but after all this is a *work* project, isn't it? On the whole, though, everyone seems happier when they're working and feeling useful.

For one thing, my group fights less when we're busy doing something.

There's a lot of pressure now about getting ready for Malaysia. Language lessons every day, slides and films about the country and its culture, history, geography, religions and races. Val did the history lecture and he told us that when Malaysia got her independence from Britain in 1957, it was predicted she would collapse as a country because she was multi-racial, multi-lingual, multi-religious and multi-cultural. Like us! But she's still hanging in together and so are we. Right on, sister countries!

We've also had visiting lecturers from universities, CUSO and the Department of External Affairs, as well as psychologists who set up simulation games. All this talk about "culture shock" is scary. They seem to be trying to prepare us for the fact that we won't fit in at first, that everything will be so different we'll be walking around stunned and out of our depth. Strangers in a strange land. (That's one of the books floating around camp. Didn't like it. But I adored *Siddhartha* and I'm next in line for *Steppenwolf*.)

First serious doubts coming up: will I be able to live in a culture so different from my own? But aren't people just people? Aren't we all human beings? Can anywhere on Earth be so different from anywhere else? I mean, it's not like they're aliens. Maya and Azahar don't have two heads a piece or anything.

*mahu*—to wish
*faham*—to understand
*chuba*—to try
*chakap*—to speak

31

*harap*—to hope
*belajar*—to learn
*tahu*—to know
*chinta*—to love

The CUSO guy made sense, though it was all so deep I got a headache from listening too hard. He talked about non-verbal communication being a major part of human interaction and each culture or group has their own unspoken signals. If you take someone from one group and put them in another, they could miss signals or misunderstand them, or send out signals that are all wrong in the new group. I suddenly got this image in my mind of us being apes or chimpanzees (should be orangutans, more appropriate to Malaysia, ha ha) and thumping your chest in one group means something totally different to thumping your chest in another. When I told this to Katie she screeched laughing and said I should've given the lecture because that was it in a nutshell. Her praise made me feel good since she's very brainy.

*sa'orang*—person
*hutan*—forest
*orangutan*—person of the forest

November 16, 1972

*M*ore trouble in my group. This is so upsetting, I feel like going home. There was a big argument about "couples" today and members were threatening to leave the group if more couples formed. It was so stupid since there's no likelihood of that happening even though a lot of the other groups are completely coupled now. Sometimes I think these arguments are just for the sake of arguing and the ones who like to argue—Katie, Ray, Lise and Darren—don't seem to realize they hurt the ones who don't—me, Claude, Louise and Cyn. Claude said nothing at first but Louise got very emotional—she took it as an attack on her and Claude—and she was so upset she started to cry. That made me cry too, for her and Claude, so I got angry, really surprised myself, and gave out hell to Ray, Darren and Katie for making all the fuss. Louise said she might leave the group and I said I would too if she did and it went on and on like that till Claude spoke up and suggested in his quiet way that perhaps it would be better if we tried to stop hatred from forming in the group instead of love. That shut everyone up and Louise and Claude went off arm in arm like two lovebirds. Sigh. Katie, Darren and Ray decided to play shuffleboard. They invited me too so I wouldn't feel left out, which I appreciated, but I didn't want to stay in their company right then.

Cyn and I went off together instead, to have a coffee. We had a hilarious discussion about which was worse, Jewish guilt or Presbyterian guilt. We talked about our families, which was neat, because a lot of the kids are rebelling against theirs, whereas Cyn feels really close to hers as I do mine, even if they do drive us crazy at times. I told her about Dad being in the hospital and having open-heart surgery this week. I don't know what was wrong with me, I guess I was feeling emotional after the meeting, but I burst out crying and couldn't stop for ages. Cyn held onto me and rocked me back and forth and she was saying these soft clucking words like a mother hen. It was so strange, because it was like she was real motherly and had a big bosom—I mean that's what it felt like—when in fact she's slim and looks like a model. When I finally stopped crying, I asked what language she was talking. She said they were Yiddish nonsense words her mother used when she had nightmares as a kid. Then she laughed and said that underneath her suave exterior was a Jewish mother dying to get out.

I felt really close to Cyn after that and I could see she was happy to have made friends too. Do all of us feel alone inside even though we're in such a big group? *Only connect,* as Val keeps saying. Cyn and I sat together at supper tonight. Katie raised her eyebrows as usually she and I sit together.

I'm going to phone Mom right now and see if there's any way I can talk to Dad before he goes into surgery.

## November 19, 1972

*O*ur group meetings were getting really bad there for a while. Floods of tears and big fights. Insensitivity towards French members came up again. We take turns now, one meeting in French, one in English. Why didn't we think of that before?! It's terrible the way we think we're giving French equal consideration when it's not that way at all. Since Katie and Darren aren't fluent that cuts down on the arguments, though Lise and Ray still go at each other and it sounds even worse in French. I'm getting better. *C'est fantastique, écouter moi-même parlant une autre langue. C'est* *merveilleux et surprenant!* And I'm even dreaming in French. *Réellement, je préfère les réunions françaises.* Claude participates more and even when I can't understand everything he's saying—his accent is very thick and his words run together—I love to hear his voice. It's so deep and relaxing, like a hot bath.

At the worst point it looked like we were going to fall apart altogether. *C'était tout fucké.* It was like everyone hated each other. The thing between Cyn and Katie finally came out. Katie was always making cutting remarks in Cyn's direction or acting as if Cyn wasn't there. I thought she was jealous of my friendship with Cyn, but Lise suddenly tackled Katie in the meeting and asked bluntly if she was anti-Semitic. It was a tense moment. I thought Cyn was going to bolt. (She told me her brothers are very political and have gone to Israel to work on the kibbutz, but she can't handle confrontation and always steers clear of it.) I also thought Katie would explode. But it didn't happen that way at all. Katie's eyes went really big, like she was stunned by what Lise had suggested, and her answer was so strong it was obviously true.

"I'm not prejudiced *that way.* It's rich people I hate."

Then Cyn got mad, it was the first time I ever saw her lose it, she's usually so reserved. (Katie says "cold" but I know better.) Cyn said that no matter what her people did, they were always in the wrong. When her grandfather emigrated from Russia and worked in a factory, the other workers were always saying he couldn't be poor since he was a Jew and they wouldn't let him in the union. Then when Cyn's dad built up his business to be really successful, he wasn't allowed in the businessmen's clubs, again because he

35

was Jewish. She said she was glad she was wealthy because at least she had some protection against the hatred, unlike poor Jews.

Things went kind of strange after that because Katie screwed up her face like she was trying not to cry and said Cyn always made her feel like she had dirt under her fingernails and that Cyn was like a lady after going to posh schools and Katie felt like a servant. I thought this was unfair because Cyn does not put on airs or anything, but I felt for Katie because she was obviously hurting. I guess Cyn felt sorry for her too because she said she never wanted to make anyone feel inferior, as no human being should ever suffer that. There was lots of crying after that and Cyn and Katie actually hugged each other, which was amazing to see. (Katie's such a hard-nosed kid and acts like a real toughie but deep down she's soft as mush. You just have to poke her a bit and it all comes out.)

All kinds of things shifted from that point, with everyone talking about prejudice and why it hurts so much, because it makes people feel like they are *worth less* or worthless just because they don't have the right amount of money or the right language or the right colour or the right name or whatever. Then Darren put in his two cents' worth and admitted that before he came on the project he didn't even know there were people in Canada who didn't own their own houses. It was such a ridiculous thing to say—I mean, what planet has he been living on—but he was being so honest and even humble for a change that we all laughed ourselves sick.

Things have really improved since that meeting. Today we each made a verbal commitment in front of the group to stick together and make things work. So far, so good. Fingers and toes crossed.

*menusia*—human
*bangsa*—race
*keluanga*—family


November 21, 1972

*C*hristmas gifts to worry about and an article for the home newspaper (my career in journalism is starting early, hurrah). And—ta dah—haircutting time! Any guy with long hair has to cut it short. Also all beards must be shaved off. Malaysia does not like hippies or drug addicts and hairy males fall into both these categories. Four guys shaved their heads right to the skin! What a laugh. But they have to wear toques all the time because their poor bald heads are freezing.

We're still short a guy for our group. Each group is supposed to be even in number, male and female, not counting the leader. Our group has such a bad reputation for fighting, no one wants to join us. Talk about rejection. The rest of the camp is down on us because we must have this guy and he must come from one of the other groups. They've closed ranks against us. That's good for them, I suppose, but not for us. We can't go to Malaysia without the right balance!

Mom phoned last night to say that Dad's still in intensive care. He told her to tell me that he's proud of me and I'm to stay on the project even though he misses his princess. He hasn't called me that for years. I didn't say anything to anyone, but I cried myself to sleep.

*rumah*—house/home
*rindu*—homesick

November 23, 1972

*V*al Trypuc is so fantastic. Things were getting heated up at the *grande réunion* last night, the French/English thing again, when he said he thought it was time to introduce *his* native language. Then he taught us how to swear in Polish. (His first name's Waldemar, I love it.) It was a scream. I can't spell half the words as they are all "zz's" and "yy's" and the "w's" are really "v's," but everyone's going around now saying *cholera jasna* and *idz do cholery* (may you die of cholera) and *psia krew* (dog's blood).

We had a big discussion on swear words and how they reflect a culture's "shadow" side, what they are most secretive or angry or repressed about. The French/English difference is amazing. All the French swear words have to do with the Roman Catholic Church. *Ostie* is the one they say all the time and it means "host," the piece of bread they take as the body of Christ. *Tabernac* and *tabernouche* refer to the tabernacle on their altars, *calice* the chalice, *chasuble* the priest's robe, and even *faux prêtre*—false priest! All our swear words are body and sex stuff—fuck, shit, cocksucker, motherfucker and so on. The worst one is "cunt." I hate that word. It's so degrading. Our biggest secret or our biggest fear? Just goes to show, the French are obsessed with

38

their religion and the English with their bodies.

It was a hilarious discussion as everyone was trying out everyone else's swear words. I nearly died when Cyn announced that *schmuck* was the Yiddish word for penis! I'll never use it again. Katie taught us this long involved curse in Gaelic that sounded so fierce you knew it could do damage. I got her to write it out, but the spelling is nothing like the pronunciation. (Malay is much easier than Irish that way.) *Go mbeidh tú ruaigthe, brúite, crúite, nite, bruite, ithe, ar leac na bpian in ifreann hiar go deo.* Which means: may you be routed, bruised, crushed, flayed, boiled and eaten on the flagstone of pain in deepest hell forever.

Wow.

So, all these curses were rising to the ceiling in a really friendly kind of way. Mom would have died if she had heard us. She won't even say "God" as it's against the First Commandment. The worst I ever heard her say was fiddlesticks. No, I just remembered that time she told Dad "not to get his balls in an uproar." It was at the dinner table and it was like a bomb landed on the chicken casserole. Dad was arguing with Daniel, over Diefenbaker of all things, and he was going red in the face. That always makes Mom nervous for his heart which is probably why she lost it and said what she did. Everyone was stunned into silence, though Gran giggled. Finally Dad said, "my dear," in a really quiet voice and Mom apologized, all flustered. But it sure ended the argument.

Louise and Cyn went to Edmonton today to do a television interview on a French talk show. All the group gathered around to wish them *bonne chance.* Good feelings all round. There was a big meeting this evening with the other groups about us needing a male. Serious bad vibes, but it made our group feel closer as we downplayed our arguments and defended each other.

"So we fight like a big close family, big deal," said Katie. She ought to know, there are twelve (!) kids in her family.

Afterwards we all hugged each other, my group I mean, as we felt so bad being the pariahs of the project. (*C'est pas cadeau.*)

*Awak benar betul.* You are right.
*Awak benar salah.* You are wrong.
*Awak benar elok.* You are beautiful.
*Saya chinta kamu.* I love you.

November 25, 1972

*A* funny thing happened in our Malay lesson today. We're taught in English since neither Maya nor Azahar speak French, so the anglophones translate whenever the francophones get stuck. Claude was sitting beside Katie and she was passing lists to him translating Malay words into French. (Her French is much better from hanging out with Jean-François. She learned the parts of the body first, ha ha.) At one point Claude let out a snort of laughter and pointed out that Katie had written one of the words in Latin not French, but it was okay as he knew what it meant. Me, like a dope, sitting next to them, said "how come you both know *Latin*?!" Even as the answer struck me before they could explain, it happened. A look went between them. It joined them together and, of course, excluded me. Recognition. They belonged to the same group, the same family, the same tribe. They're both Roman Catholics. It was weird, because until that moment it was obvious they were separate and different: she, an English-speaking Newfoundlander; he, a French-speaking Québecois. Then suddenly, there was this accord, this cord that linked them together. You could see it in their eyes. It was still there at our group meeting tonight, that unspoken acceptance of each other, like they'll listen more to each other now because they know they're joined that way.

It's exactly what Val talks about! "Only connect," he keeps saying, again and again. "No matter how different you are from each other, find the connection. There will always be at least one and it builds a bridge where you can meet and begin to understand each other. Learn to do it here, now, and you will be able to do it in Malaysia."

By the way, Katie wrote *satis* to translate *chukup* instead of *assez* for "enough." I got the word from her a while ago. Wow, my first word in Latin. Imagine knowing an ancient language like that.

"I keep forgetting you're a Prod," she said to me.

We had a great talk about Roman Catholics and Protestants. (She laughs at me for saying "Roman" all the time.) In Newfoundland all the schools are separated by religion, with separate Protestant schools for Salvation Army, Methodist, Anglican and so on, as well as the Roman Catholic ones. The two of us freaked out when we realized that even though we both know a few Catholic and Protestant families, we've never hung around with them. She's my first Catholic friend and I'm her first Protestant one! Who would ever have believed it. I mean, the things

41

you don't notice. Talk about walking around with blinkers on and half-asleep (Val).

We decided to tackle the matter.

"What do you know about Catholics?" she asked me.

Not wanting to offend her, I kept quiet about worshipping statues and saints, and being under the thumb of priests and popes.

"Well, you believe in transubstantiation, right?" I said, remembering what I was taught in Sunday School.

"What's that when it's at home?" was her reply.

"So what do you know about Protestants?" I demanded.

Needless to say, she was less diplomatic.

"You have ugly churches with no decorations, you can't drink, sing or dance, and you've got something against the Mother of God."

Talk about prejudices. As it turned out, we didn't know anything about each other. We had to laugh.

'alam—universe
nyawa—life/spirit
Tuhan—God


November 27, 1972

Up early today for a lecture on Malaysian etiquette. Don't put your feet up or in front of anyone's face, that is the height of insult. Don't stand higher than others, if they sit you sit, if they lounge, you lounge. Eat at the same pace as everyone else, you can't finish first but have to keep eating as long as everyone else is. Eat with your right hand if there are no utensils, never never—*jangan! jamais!*—use the left. The left hand is to splash water on your privates after going to the bathroom. Picking your nose is okay! Burping after a meal is okay too, even a compliment. ("Chest-thumping," Katie whispered to me.) There are different ways to shake hands among Muslim Malays. Men and women don't shake hands with each other, only men to men and women to women. When I shake hands with girls or women, I touch my hand to my heart after the shake. For older women, as a special mark of respect, I cup both my hands over theirs or into theirs and then with both hands touch my heart. So beautiful and gracious, I can't wait to try it on Gran.

I hope I remember all this stuff when I get there. That's the worst with cultural differences. You could be offering someone a terrible insult without knowing it. They don't like dogs (can't remember why) so *makan anjing*, eat dog, is a swear word. *Makan taik*, eat shit, is another one. Must remember to forget those.

Val gave us the talk, as he said it would have been discourteous to ask Maya or Azahar to do it. I'm beginning to get a sense of a culture that is much older and more sensitive than ours, so much more aware of how people treat each other. We must seem like clods to them, loud and crude. Like in *Passage to India*. (Val passed around copies for us to read. I *will* be Mrs. Moore some day.)

In the afternoon my group hitchhiked to Edmonton to see the city. The girls paired off with guys in case of rapists. I went with Darren as neither Katie nor Cyn would (they still can't stand him). Louise went with Claude, of course, and Ray and Lise went together in an effort to be friendlier

43

with each other. (Things are improving in the group but it ain't perfect yet.) Darren's okay, but I find it hard to talk with him one-to-one. I mean, he's so good-looking, when I stare into those baby blues I can't keep my mind on what I'm saying.

Edmonton is a neat, clean and orderly city. Dad would love it. Even the trees are tidy. Everything's in numbers and squares. All the buildings look new, with straight lines and wide glass windows. Nice slow pace too. (I prefer Ottawa, though, because of the older architecture and the Rideau Canal.) We went to the Art Gallery which had a special show of Krieghoff's paintings of Quebec. I really liked them but I thought the modern section had a lot of ugly stuff. I mean, what are you supposed to feel when you look at coloured stripes on a canvas? *Rien.* Then we went to a park that had a frozen lake set in its centre like a bowl of ice. It was a cold sunny day and there were people skating. I took a photo of some little kids muffled up in scarves and mittens. We fooled around on the ice and I pushed Ray over a few times. The two of us wrestled and took pictures of each other.

We're staying overnight at Ray's house. I like his younger brother, but his parents are odd, very cold or something. The family are like strangers living together. They don't seem to talk to each other but only to us, the outsiders. Ray acts differently here, not his usual lively self, like he's walking on egg shells. The house is nice, like ours only bigger, but Katie keeps saying how huge it is and how rich they must be.

I'm writing this in Ray's sister's room. She's in Toronto studying law at Osgoode Hall. Brains don't run in this family, they gallop. Katie is poking around like a real nosy parker. She says she can't imagine living in such luxury. She doesn't even have her own bed, never mind her own room, but shares with two sisters. She says she always wanted to be an only child of rich parents, like some of the Shirley Temple movies, but instead she's one of twelve and her family's on welfare. Her dad's a fisherman but he hurt his back in a boating accident and is on disability. He started drinking because of that and it sounds as if it's been downhill for the family ever since. (Katie says, "The situation's hopeless, but not serious." A Newfoundland proverb?)

I'm going to stop writing because I want to talk to her. We haven't had a heart-to-heart for a while. Sometimes I really worry about her. She drinks a lot for a little person. (Jean-François calls her "the Irish bathtub." He should talk.) But it's not just that. It's these moods she gets into. Real black. Her eyes go kind of cloudy and it's like she's lost somewhere far away and she can't find her way back. I mean, she's so bright, thinking all the time and questioning everything and fighting against the world. She's a real fighter, and then this other thing comes over her. Like she's lost the battle and given up. It breaks my heart to see her like that.

November 30, 1972

We're saved! Val has decided to bring in a new male participant off the waiting list so our group will be big enough. It's too late for him to join us, but we'll meet him at the airport. Since he's missed the training camps, we'll have to help him out. His name is Dave Honey (I love

45

it) and he's from Medicine Hat. Must be cute with a name like that. Katie and I are already arguing over who gets him, ha ha.

Our group finished the new cabin today. I had a paint fight with Ray. Paint all over my hair, face, hands, clothes. What a mess. The other guys kept telling us to stop horsing around, but we ignored them.

A sad thing happened in our group meeting today. Darren was sulking and refused to participate. I think he was still hurt from the others not wanting to hitch to Edmonton with him. There were a few comments made in his direction about "Mr. High and Mighty" and "getting down from his high horse" and then it happened. He cracked. Like Humpty Dumpty falling off the wall. He didn't look at any of us but kept staring over our heads, and he spoke in a distant kind of voice. He said his parents divorced when he was five and when they weren't using him as their battlefield, they shipped him off to boarding school. He's been on his own all his life. He thought by joining this project he might belong to something at last but instead, he kept saying and doing all the wrong things so he was still alone.

Then he started to sob. It was terrible. His whole body shook with dry heaves. I mean, he didn't even know how to cry. We sat frozen, looking at him. It was so unlike him to lose control, so awful to see. Suddenly Claude got up and put his arms around him and held him like a father and said, "*C'est okay, mon frère.* You are with us. *Nous sommes ta famille.*" Darren was able to cry, then. Such a flood of sadness. Such grief. We all went over and practically smothered him in a group hug, everyone in tears till we were all laughing and crying at the same time. Phew. Total emotion-city.

Later I said to Katie, "Do we crack one by one? Am I next?"

"Fat chance," she said, real casual. "You've been bawling since you got here. You're scrambled eggs already, kiddo."

What a pal.

*abang*—elder brother
*kakak*—elder sister
*adek*—young brother/sister

December 2, 1972

*H*APPY 18TH BIRTHDAY KATIE DALY! *BON ANNIVERSAIRE!*

Slept in till noon today because I had a bad earache. Must have been the pillow fight with Ray yesterday. Malay lesson after lunch, then a simulation game in the recreation room till supper. The theme was prejudice and the whole thing was very emotional and upsetting. At one point we were sitting in a big circle and we had to move around according to how we answered certain questions, e.g., "Is your neighbour the same colour as you?" or "Is your best friend the same religion as you?" and so on and so forth. By the end of it, Cyn ended up sitting alone as did Marcus, the only black guy on the project, along with Jenny, the Chinese group leader and Betty. We could all see quite plainly without the facilitators saying anything how minority groups are isolated in general society.

It was an amazing experience, especially when each of the ones sitting on their own decided to say something even though the facilitators made it clear they didn't have to, that "the game was over." It was a big step for Cyn, I knew, since she always keeps quiet in this kind of situation. (We're all changing and that's the simple fact of it.) She didn't say a lot, but when she was finished she squared her shoulders and held her head real proud and said, "I am a Jew." I caught my breath. She was like a queen.

Marcus talked about being an army brat (his dad's stationed in North Bay) and how, as a kid, he always ignored the fact he was black, as if it were an accident. Then the Black Power movement started in the States and suddenly he realized he had something to be proud of. He started reading books by Malcolm X and Angela Davis and did his own research into his family background. The worst thing he said was that white Canadians assumed they were the true Canadians because of their colour even though their families weren't in the country as long as his! His ancestors came to Nova Scotia after the Civil War in America, when a lot of black people settled here. He was never taught this at school. It was as if his people didn't exist.

I remember learning about when the French, the British, the Scottish, the Irish and the Germans came here. All white people. But I was never taught about black people coming here. It's crazy. How come I know all the kings of England and the geography of the United States and I know *dick all* about my own country?!

Jenny emigrated to Canada when she was a teenager. She described what it was like to come to a strange country, how she was homesick all the time and how she didn't feel accepted by other Canadians except for Chinese ones. She particularly hated people telling her all the time that "her

English was good" (the French kids nodded at that), as if language was the only thing that mattered, the only thing that made you a person.

Betty's talk was the most painful, because it was the worst. She and her brother were taken away from their family and put into a Christian "home" that was supposedly a school but was really a prison for kids from the reserve. They told her that "being an Indian was dirty and savage." They wanted to turn her into a little white girl. It was obvious to her that they had no love for her or her people, saw nothing good in her race or culture. She was always lonely and thought the world was a terrible place. Her brother rebelled and tried to run away but he was beaten and locked in a room. She just waited and counted the years till she was old enough to return home. Gawd, it was a horrible story. Listening to her, I was ashamed of being a Christian and a Canadian. How can these things happen in a country that is supposed to be democratic and civilized?

Sometimes I think all the stuff I'm discovering and learning is growing inside me like a bonfire that's getting bigger and bigger and brighter and brighter. A pure fire that's burning away so much junk and so many bad ideas, leaving me brighter and purer myself. I wonder if this is what the Reverend Merry means when he talks about a "baptism of fire"?

At supper, Claude wheeled out a giant birthday cake on a tea table and everyone sang "Happy Birthday" to Katie in French and English. She looked like she was going to bawl at first, then recovered enough to demand kisses from every guy in the place. What a kid. Then we threw her in the snow and gave her eighteen bumps. I gave her my green beret that she's always borrowing which looks fantastic with her red hair. Darren and Ray went halfers on a bottle of Irish whiskey. Cyn gave her a pair of dangly earrings with stars and moons, gorgeous. Louise and Claude made the birthday cake and Lise gave her a carton of cigarettes. I asked her what Jean-François gave her and she winked and said she was getting it later with a big red bow on it, har. (Guess it does get better with time.) But actually he had written home to get her his favourite album by Renée Claude, "*Je Reprends Mon Souffle*," with a double cover with all the lyrics and a note inside saying "*pour mon amour irlandais, un espace vert de mon pays.*" Sigh. So romantic. All in all it was a good haul and she said it was the best birthday she ever had in her life. Needless to say she's not in her own bed tonight, so I'm writing this without interruptions for a change.

*Baik*—good
*Baik-lah!*—good one!
You hold up your thumb and shout *baik-lah!*

December 3, 1972

*M*alay Way Day
       Girls served guys at meals, then ate later. We all ate with our hands—right only! No swearing, smoking, touching or kissing in public. Girls walked behind guys outside. (We used this as an opportunity to clobber them with snowballs down their necks and backs. *Baik-lah!*) Everyone spoke as much Malay as possible. I'm taking extra lessons with Katie. She and Ray and Lise are practically fluent at

this point. Meals were eaten sitting on the floor with table-cloths spread in a long line. We moved all the tables and chairs against the walls, to the horror of the kitchen staff. Same for dinner. I'm sure it's easier eating by hand with Malaysian food, rice and things, but with mashed potatoes and turnips it's messy!

Maya got upset at some of the stuff we were doing. (The whole day was our own idea and Val went along with it.) She got the girls together to have a talk. She said that women don't serve men in Malaysia any more or less than we do here. After all, it's our mothers who do all the cook-ing, shopping, laundry and stuff. She said a group of Malay girls would not be waiting on guys hand and foot like we were. And she said that girls and guys were not as separated in Malaysia as we thought. We would see that ourselves when we went to the youth clubs where Malaysian girls and boys work together.

Then she asked us for our general impression of the posi-tion of women in Malaysia. We all agreed it looked pretty bad what with arranged marriages and all. She said we were making judgements about right ways and wrong ways instead of thinking in terms of *different ways* to do things. She said who's to say which is better or worse, arranged mar-riages or self-chosen ones? The West is notorious for divorce and broken homes. Who can measure the quantity of hap-piness or unhappiness produced by either system? Then she said it was all relative to country or culture, especially the position of women, as women everywhere have to struggle for their rights and no culture can be said to have reached the point where women are equal. She talked about her job and all the difficulties she had as a career woman. Then she said she talked to women journalists in Canada and they had the same problems; men not taking them seriously, not promoting them, not paying them as well.

She said it would be both harder and easier for us as women to cross the cultural barrier in Malaysia. Easier because the women there will accept us as we are and not judge us. But harder because men everywhere look on women from different cultures as exotic sex objects and not people in their own right. It was always happening to her when she travelled to other countries. She would be welcomed by women but chased by men who kept telling her she was "exciting" because she was "different." (This pissed her off, you could tell.)

It was another one of those great discussions which really made me wonder. Are human beings totally screwed up or what? Why is it so hard for people just to be people and to respect each other?

I realized something else from that talk. Maya disagrees with some of the stuff Azahar tells us and vice versa. She is an Indian woman, he is a Malay man. She's Hindu. He's Muslim. And there's still the Chinese to meet as well. No one person or group can say, "This is Malaysia." It's more than a single thing, like our project. There isn't any one of us who can say, "I am Canada." But all of us together are closer to the mark, all of us together can say, "We are Canada."

December 4, 1972

*A* government guy from Ottawa showed up today. He held meetings with Val and the group leaders, then mingled with the rest of us. I told him he looked like Prime Minister Trudeau (no kidding, he did, kinda cute) and he said I looked like Margaret. What a dope. She's half my size. Had an argument with Katie about her, actually. Katie says Maggie is just a middle-class airhead and a spoiled brat. I don't agree at all. I think she's a real individual, trying to stay true to herself in the midst of a bureaucratic nightmare. And it was all so romantic in the beginning.

"He should have married Barbra Streisand," Katie declared.

"An American?!" I was aghast.

But at least the argument cheered Katie up (that's my girl). I found her in our cabin lying on her bed, writing out place-names from home: Job's Cove, Heart's Desire, Juniper Stump, Heart's Content, Leading Tickles, Heart's Delight, Twillingate, Forest Field, L'Anse au Loup, Harbour Grace...

"Got it bad?" I asked gently.

"Newfoundlanders always miss the Rock," she sniffed. "The way the Irish miss Ireland."

She told me that her grandmother brought a little packet of earth over from Ireland when they emigrated, to mix with the Canadian soil in their garden. I wonder if Dad's people did the same when they came from Scotland? Must ask him.

## December 6, 1972

Nearly finished my Christmas presents. I'm knitting a shawl for Gran, rose-coloured wool with green speckles. Beautiful. I work away during meetings and lectures now. (Lise calls me Madame Defarge.) Crocheted a tie for Dad and antimacassars for Mom's favourite armchair. I've saved up some money for Matthew as he'll need cash when he goes to university next year, but I hadn't a clue what to give Daniel till Betty gave me a terrific idea. She came over to me in the recreation room to admire my crochet work and asked where I had learned to do it. I explained that Mrs. Merry, the minister's wife, used to teach us after Sunday School. Betty asked me to show her how and since I had extra needles I got her started on a doily. The next day she taught me how to string beads on a hand-loom to make a necklace and how to sew beads on a leather circle to make a pendant. Perfect for Daniel!

I've drawn a simple picture on a piece of leather, a bird on a telephone wire. It's Daniel's favourite Leonard Cohen song, he's always singing it, "A Bird on the Wire." He'll be out of his brains with joy when he gets this, what do you bet.

December 7, 1972

*Selamat pagi.*—Good morning.
*Selamat tengah hari.*—Good afternoon.
*Selamat petang.*—Good evening.
*Selamat malam.*—Good night.

*T*his morning we had a lecture from a professor on the history of Islam. Wow, the Islamic Empire used to cover practically the entire world. How come I never heard of it? All I was taught about was the Roman Empire and the British Empire. This keeps happening to me and I'm getting really angry. I worked hard at school and did well—why do I know next to nothing?

It was very interesting because the professor, Dr. Riaz from Pakistan, started off by asking if we were familiar with Islam, Muhammed and Muslims. We all nodded yes, of course, and then he asked us what exactly we knew. Now that was the funny part, because I was sure I knew something—I mean, the words are so familiar—but when we got down to the specifics, like me and Katie with Catholics and Protestants, it turned out we had no information at all!

One of the guys said, "Well, women are considered inferior," which made the girls laugh because of our talk with Maya. Dr. Riaz nodded and said, yes, this is what the West says while it treats its own women badly, but that anyone who studies Islam discovers differently. He handed out copies of the Qur'an in English and asked us to share them around and read as much as possible.

Then he talked about the Prophet Muhammed and the beginning of Islam. It was wonderful. I mean, I expected to be bored and ended up not even knitting. You could tell Dr. Riaz is a devout Muslim—which means "one who submits to God"—because his face shone when he was talking, like he was in love. The story of the Prophet was amazing, a fantastic tale from the Arabian Nights except it was true! Muhammed must have been guided by God. How else could he have done what he did? Driven out of Mecca with only a few followers, mostly women and slaves, and six years later he rode back in without a fight, Islam already established in other countries. He sounds like the kings in the Bible, kind to women and orphans, wise in government

55

and successful at war against the odds. By the time Dr. Riaz had finished, I knew that Muhammed was one of the greatest men in history and I could only wonder, once again, why I was never told about him. (Borrowed Lise's copy of Kahlil Gibran's *The Prophet*, but it's not about Muhammed though it's very spiritual and beautiful. Are there books about Muhammed in English, I wonder?)

*Salaam Alaykum* (Arabic)—God be with you. Muslim greeting for both hello and goodbye.

## December 8, 1972

We had our Christmas party yesterday since the camp breaks up next week and Azahar and Maya are going home tomorrow. Everyone got dolled up for the event. Katie is a real wild dresser when she doesn't wear jeans and sweaters. She wore a black lace mini-dress and black stockings and frizzed out her hair like a burning bush. The guys' eyes popped out when they saw her. Especially Darren. (*Très intéressant.* He kept asking her to dance every time Jean-François went to the bathroom, which was quite often since *le garçon* was drinking beer by the gallon.) I dressed more conservatively (natch) in my dark-blue velvet, but I combed out my hair instead of tying it back for a change. Ray kept playing with it and saying that he could drown in it and stuff like that. I pushed him away but not too seriously.

Val was Santa Claus which sent everyone into hysterics because his paunch fit perfectly. Maya and Azahar were presented with illustrated books of Canada which all of us had chipped in for. The kitchen staff gave out Camp Heart pennants and a special gift for Claude, a bottle of Beaujolais. He gave each of them a red rose. (Love that guy.) There was a joke gift for Val, a copy of Dr. Spock's *Baby and Child Care* signed by every participant, with comments in French and English. And of course each group leader got something outrageous from their group. Lise laughed at the riding crop we gave her and said she would use it on her horse *aussi*. After the speeches and presentations, we all linked arms and sang "You've Got a Friend." Very emotional, loads of hugs and tears.

Then the fun began. There was oodles of booze but I didn't drink a drop, I was out to hop and bop. Everyone danced together, all over the floor. You didn't have to ask anyone to dance or wait for anyone to ask you. Val was the deejay using a hired sound system and a great mix of records; Blood, Sweat and Tears, Buffalo Springfield, the Beatles, the Stones, Joni Mitchell, Ian and Sylvia, Janis Joplin, Bruce Cockburn, Cat Stevens. The best party of my life!

Later our group had a nightcap in the guys' cabin, eggnog with Southern Comfort. Yum. But I only had one. I've decided I don't want to drink, not when I see the effect it has on people I love (read: Daniel and Katie). Plus, it makes people fight. I mean, I couldn't believe it, there we were, happy together after an incredible evening, and next minute an argument crops up. Lise and Ray against Darren. Darren was drunk and he seemed to be making up for that time he cracked because he was putting the programme down and saying it was all "commie propaganda" and we were being "brain-washed." Lise said if there was ever a brain that needed washing, it was his. After a bit of shouting and whatnot, the party broke up. They were all drunk anyway. Katie had gone off with Jean-François so she wasn't in on it. (Hey, I wonder if that's what was eating Darren? Hmm. The plot thickens. Watch this space.) Katie got stoned on LSD tonight, the dummy. I was so mad at her, that kind of stuff scares me to death.

"Why did you do it?" I asked her, really upset.

She said she has to try everything once before she dies.

"Would you walk into a fire?" I demanded.

"If someone showed me how, yes!"

I mean, what can you say to that?

I wasn't feeling too good after that crummy ending to the party, when Ray came over to my cabin. I was almost asleep but he plopped down on the edge of my bed so I sat up to talk to him. He was tipsy but not out of his skull and he said he needed to unload about his family. Poor kid. No wonder he's mixed up. I had no idea stuff like that happened in normal homes. (So what's normal?) And you can't go to the police or anyone when it's your own relations, can you? Why didn't his parents notice who was going into their kids' bedrooms? Why did they ignore Ray when he tried to tell them? I mean, if your parents won't listen, who can you go to with that kind of shit? No one. I put my arms around him to make him feel better. What with one thing and another, we started necking. It was great, he's a terrific kisser, and I think something might have happened except that someone woke up and called out, "What the fuck is going on?" so we knocked it off. (Nobody makes out in the cabins with everyone else there. Couples hide out in the empty ones.)

I'm writing this out matter-of-factly to try and get a clear and calm picture of what's happening. But the truth is I'm very confused and upset. Ray thanked me today for "being there for him" but didn't mention our kissing. I didn't know what to say and muttered something about "friends." Really, I don't know how I feel about him. He's more like a brother, though obviously our kidding around all the time means something else. Katie kept saying, "You know what wrestling leads to," but I was pretending to myself that I didn't. One part of me wants a boyfriend, and I do like him a lot, but the idea of being a couple in our group really puts me off. Look at the hassle Louise and Claude had to put up with—and from Ray too!

I feel so mixed up right now. I want to run away and hide. And I don't feel like talking to anyone. I wish I was back at home in my own room where I could close the door on the world and listen to my favourite Joni Mitchell album.

### December 10, 1972

*P*hone call from Mom this morning. Dad's out of intensive care and will be home when I get there! Thank you, God! That really made my day. *Nothing* could have happened today to upset me after that.

We finished the last job for Camp Heart this afternoon. The recreation room has a brand new coat of paint. All the groups worked on it and there was no fooling around as each group wanted to prove to the others that they could work as a team. Malay lesson after that. It was sad doing it without Azahar and Maya, but we're keeping up the conversations and going over vocabulary ourselves.

*Saya pandai chakap melayu? Ya! Saya suka Bahasa Malaysia dan saya harap saya akan chakap dengan banyak orang₂—kawan₂!—di Malaysia bila saya tinggal disitu.*

Late afternoon was official free time, but *Le Gang de Lise* (that's what we call ourselves now, I guess we've finally accepted our leader, har) met together in one of the classrooms. *La réunion était en français et il y avait beaucoup de bon sentiment.* Claude showed us his slides from the time he worked as a logger around Baie James, *encore en français et j'ai compris la plupart!* (My head is full of words in different languages. *Je pense que saya akan jalan sou! Mais saya chinta!*)

The slides were breathtaking, a grand tour of the French-Canadian Shield. I didn't know the Laurentians, *Les Laurentides*, were the oldest mountain range in the world! Slide after slide showed a majestic wilderness; vast tracts of forest like heaps of ink-black lace, a chain of silver lakes scattered over muskeg bogs, white rushing rivers crashing down crag and rock, herds of caribou roaming wild. I felt my soul expand as I gazed on the images that were my country. I could only think that if Quebec is lost to us, we will lose our heart's blood.

The group had talked beforehand, *en français*, about French-English relations. I was so embarrassed to haltingly explain that whenever I thought of French-Canadians I had in mind Marie Chapdelaine picking blueberries, or the *coureurs-de-bois* portaging through the wilds with fur-skins and canoes on their backs. Lise snorted with disgust, but

Claude burst into laughter. I'm glad he spoke slowly because the point he made was so good. He said that the English view of French-Canadians was frozen in the past because that was the last time our two cultures related to each other. He said the great chasm between us is a modern one because English Canada knows little or nothing about modern French-Canadian culture—their popular singers, film-makers, actors, talk-show hosts and writers. Even as he said it I was struck by the truth. Though Quebec is so near to me, I never heard of Renée Claude till Jean-François gave Katie the album, nor have I ever watched French television! I know some of their politicians but none of their artists. *C'est terrible. C'est tragique. Moi, j'ai besoin de faire quelque chose échanger cette situation. Premièrement, je vais lire le livre que Claude a donné au group*—Les Nègres Blancs d'Amérique.

The meeting ended with a spontaneous mini-cultural show! Louise sang a beautiful sad ballad about Louis Riel, which he wrote himself, in prison, before he was hanged. Then she, Claude and Lise taught us the chorus of a French-Canadian song so we could join in between all the verses. *Danse, mon moin', danse!* Katie did a hilarious imitation of "Don Messer's Jubilee" and danced a hornpipe to the rest of us singing "I'se the B'y that Builds the Boat." I told one of Bernie Bedore's stories about Joe Mufferaw, the giant of Renfrew County. Cyn told a Yiddish folk-tale about a *golem*, a creature made of clay and air. Last but not best (har) came Ray and Darren. They sang a thundering rendition of "They All Call It Canada," with hands on their breasts. Utterly atrocious.

## December 14, 1972

*U*p at 8:30 a.m. and got ready to leave. Departure from Camp Heart at 10:30 a.m. I was in a quiet mood, sad and nostalgic as I knew something had ended. The training period is over. There will be no more lessons, no more discussions, no more preparations. Like birds pushed out of the nest, soon we will fly to Malaysia to put what we have learned to the test. It is done. We are either ready or we are not.

A bus took us to the train station in Edmonton. I couldn't keep up the quiet mood for long. Katie and Ray were play-acting in the back seat, pretending they were a nun and a priest in charge of the rest of us on a school outing. It went straight into improvised theatre and was very raunchy and blasphemous. They entertained us for the entire trip. Ray was particularly good considering he's not even R.C. He said he loves all the Father Bing Crosby movies. What a card.

At the train station, the Eastern kids said goodbye to the Western kids as we were travelling in opposite directions. Everyone was kissing and hugging each other and shouting "*Joyeux Noël*" and "See you next year." Ray caught me completely by surprise. He pulled me away from the crowd and gave me a long deep kiss. Then he held my face in his hands and stared at me intensely and said, "I'll miss you. Write to me." I was stunned. I mean, he had been acting so casual right up to that. Then he ran out of the station and that was him gone. I wish he didn't live in Edmonton. At least we would have had some time travelling together.

I must have looked shaken when I got on the train because Katie asked me if I was okay. I shrugged and said nothing. Later I had a sip of Lonesome Charlie wine with her and Jean-François in their berth. They look so cute together. He's really good-looking, petite like her, with dark-brown hair and big brown eyes and a pixie face. They look like kids, but not so innocent, ha ha. Katie invited me to join them, as she could tell I was feeling down. They smoked marijuana too, but not me. Katie tried to get me to talk, but I didn't want to, so I came back here to my own berth to write in my journal.

The frozen prairies are rattling past, outside the window. The sky is grey and heavy with unshed snow. The train is making that clickety-clack, chucka-chucka noise I love. Soothing to the troubled heart. I guess that's what I've got, a troubled heart. I really don't know what to make of Ray or my feelings for him. One thing I do know for certain, I don't want to get involved with him unless I'm sure of my feelings. He's had enough bad stuff in his life to deal with, I'm not going to add to his hurt. So, do I love him or not? It's a simple question. How come I can't answer it?

And is this a good idea, I ask you, going off to Malaysia in a state of emotional confusion? Jesse McKinnock, you are one dodo brain. Have you learned NOTHING?

## December 25, 1972

*M*ERRY CHRISTMAS HO HO HO.
Funny how Christmas is never the way it's built up to be, not since I was thirteen anyway. That's the year I slept in for the first time and didn't bother to get up till breakfast. I still love it, though: the coloured lights in the

window sparkling on the snow; the smells in the house—
pine needles, roast turkey, hot fruit punch with nutmeg
and cinnamon; the aunts and uncles trooping in to visit,
shaking the snow off their coats, stamping their feet.

It's great to see Dad out of bed, though he has to stay in
his chair wrapped up in a rug. He looks a bit grey, but his
eyes are as bright and sparky as ever. He said he thought he
was a goner after that last attack and he was grateful to be
here. I can hear them all downstairs, Mom and Dad, Gran,
my aunts and uncles. They're eating Christmas cake and
drinking tea. My brothers have gone out with their girlfriends. A dry Christmas is not their idea of fun, and once
dinner is over, they're history.

When Daniel saw his pendant, he let out a whoop and
gave me a bear hug. Dad raised his eyebrows and said next
year I'd be giving him earrings. Daniel opened his mouth
to argue, then shut it again as he looked at Dad, so thin
and pale. Dad noticed him noticing and looked angry for a
minute, then he grinned.

"So I finally got the last word around here, eh?"

Everyone laughed and Mom looked relieved. She slipped
Daniel a few extra dollars in the kitchen. (Not like him to
be so tactful.)

Snow is falling outside, thickly and silently. The window
is decorated with frost. I'm sitting on my bed, listening to
my *Blue* album, feeling melancholy. It's my own fault.
Shirley called earlier and invited me over to her house. A lot
of the gang are there, but I don't feel like going. I don't
know what it is, but I just can't take my friends right now. I
couldn't sit and listen to the dumb stuff they talk about and
I'd probably end up fighting with someone, like at Derek's

Christmas party. They were telling racist jokes and I saw red and got very upset. Everyone said I was getting too serious and had lost my sense of humour. But how can I ignore jokes that insult the people I love? I mean, they were horrible jokes against Val, Marcus, Cyn, Betty, Katie...

Shirley was saying on the phone that I've really changed and I don't fit in any more. She said I'm making judgements on everyone like they're not good enough for me. I guess she's right. But it's not that I feel superior—really, I feel lonely and shaky—but it's true that I'm not the person I was before I went on the project. It opened my eyes to so much stuff. How can I close them again because it's uncomfortable to see?

I wish I could talk to Katie or Cyn. They'd understand. Or anyone from my group. Boy, do I ever miss those guys. I can't wait to see them again. Katie wrote to me from Dildo, a long letter about her family. They had to get Christmas baskets from the church as they had no money for presents or dinner. She went into this whole political thing about how Newfoundland should never have joined Confederation in 1949 because the province wasn't poor until that happened. They've lost hundreds of thousands of people to mainland emigration and they have no control over their own resources like the Grand Banks and Labrador's hydro. She doesn't want to be a British colony, but thinks they should have gone independent or even joined Ireland, the way Saint Pierre and Miquelon are part of France. She should go into politics. She would really shake up Ottawa.

I also got a letter from Ray. Heavy. Even though I half expected something like this, it's still like a bolt out of the blue. He says he was attracted to me from the start but he could tell I wasn't interested so he didn't pursue it. Am I blind or what?! I keep going back over the whole thing, but except for the wrestling I'd've had to be a mind-reader to know he was interested in me. He says he feels he has always known me and that he has never felt so at ease with a girl in his life. Then he finished the letter in capitals with "JESSE, YOU ARE AN INCREDIBLE PERSON AND I AM HONOURED TO KNOW YOU."

Knock me down with a feather.

I was very careful when I wrote back. I'd actually been thinking about this since that long kiss in Edmonton when I knew without a doubt that he was serious about me. I guess I'm too practical to walk into trouble when I can spot it a mile away. We've got to spend three months in Malaysia together. It's going to take all our effort and energy to meet the demands of the project and open ourselves to the Malaysian way of life. The last thing we need is to be involved in a heavy-duty relationship. Yes, I care about him, yes, he's very important to me and yes, I am *so* happy that he will be there with me, but I want us to work together as friends and group members.

That's what I wrote to him, though it hurt me to do it.

In a way, I think I might be sorry. Ray is the only guy in the project that I'm attracted to. Well, not counting Claude, who's taken, and Darren. (But Darren's just a physical thing and you'd have to be dead not to be attracted to him. Even Katie admits he's gorgeous and she hates him.) I've never had a real boyfriend. Sixteen is the age-limit for dating in this house (Stone Age) so I've only been out alone with guys this year, not counting church picnics and stuff with the Sunday School gang. As for Ian, Darryl and Mark, forget it. Non-events.

The truth is, though, I'm not ready for a serious commitment like going steady or whatever. Maybe if I was in love I'd feel differently? Or is that a load of phony baloney in romance books and comics? Anyway, my mind's made up. I don't want to be Ray's girlfriend and I had to let him down as gently as possible so things won't be too awful when we meet up again. What a turnabout though. Me giving the brush-off to such a good-looking and brainy guy. Who would ever have thought? Sometimes I think I'm changing so much even I don't recognize myself! I guess if I could look into the future I'm probably doing more stuff that I could never imagine myself doing. Wonder who I'll be in Malaysia?

## January 1st *1973*

*H*APPY NEW YEAR! 1973 IS THE YEAR FOR ME! No time to write. Dinner's ready downstairs. More turkey, groan. Then I'm off to Shirley's for the post-mortem on her party last night. It was fantastic. I actually necked with Mark! (Was he surprised.) Counting down the days till I'm back on the project. This time next week I'll be flying out of here!

## January 6, 1973
## Montreal Airport

*M*ALAYSIA OR BUST! I'm writing this in the waiting lounge as our flight is delayed due to the blizzard. Ray and Katie have gone off in search of food while I look after the hand luggage. I'm glad I decided to keep my journal with me. I'm going to write down everything as it happens, the plane trip, the stopover in London, the long trek across the Middle East and India to Kuala Lumpur, the capital of Malaysia…

Despite all my worries, things are fine with Ray. It was so funny. When I saw him standing there at the departure gates in his orange parka, looking like the all-Canadian boy, I thought, "Wow, he's really cute and he could be my boyfriend." Then he spotted me and his face lit up. I was really happy to see him and we did a great imitation of that commercial, "The closer he gets, the better you look." We ran towards each other with our arms out wide and swung each other around and started wrestling. Just like old times. He didn't mention our letters and neither did I.

It was so far-out to see my group again! Gawd, how important these guys are to me. Katie and I screeched when we saw each other and I swung *her* around, the little shrimp. Cyn and I hugged like mad and then Lise and Louise and Claude and Darren. Boy, for a group who are always fighting we sure put on a show of affection. The other kids were actually staring at us, we were making such a fuss.

Val Trypuc came over with this guy in tow and introduced Dave Honey. Well, I'm afraid the name was a red herring. A bit of a disappointment in the looks department. When he was being introduced, Katie and I avoided each other's eyes so we wouldn't giggle. (We were fighting over this guy?) My first reaction was, "Oh no, he's the kind of kid who sits in the back of the class." Sloppy dresser, greasy hair, slumped shoulders, thick glasses. We all felt sorry for him being thrown into the deep end like this, without knowing anyone or being prepared for Malaysia, so we tried to tell him about the training camps and stuff. I can hardly believe it, he actually looked *bored* after a while and excused himself and went to sit down and read. I was taken aback and so were the others, but Katie grinned and shrugged. "Great. A total odd bod. He's in the right group." I can see him from here, underneath the flight monitor, completely oblivious to all of us milling around, his nose stuck in *By the Banks of the Baram*, one of Val's Malaysian books. (My name's on the list for it. I guess Dave got first dibs being an emergency case.)

And here they come, my favourite people, Ray and Katie, with armloads of French fries and Coke. Yabba dabba doo.


Later, on the plane, waiting for take-off:

They're de-icing the wings again and the blizzard seems to be easing up. Hopefully we'll be leaving soon. Ta dah— a dream come true—I got the window seat. Actually, it's Katie's, but she changed with me once I promised I wouldn't object if she and Jean-François neck. They just got back together and won't see each other in Malaysia. I said *pas de problème*, I understood. Hah! I would have agreed to anything to get the window seat. Ray has the one in front of me and he reaches back to grab me from time to time. He's trying to catch some sleep right now, as he's exhausted from being up early and having to fly from Alberta. All the Western kids look tired. It's kind of crazy that they're flying backwards around the world, when Malaysia's nearer to them across the Pacific. Ours is not to wonder why, just to do or die. Still, I'm glad we're all going together.

Omigod, the captain is announcing that we are on our way! I'm going to die. The engines are gearing up, roaring away. The whole plane's shuddering into motion. We're sliding down the runway. I'm going to keep writing in here as we go up because I am scared witless. Ridiculous as it may seem in this day and age, this is the first time I have ever been on an airplane. The stewardesses are running down the aisle. Is there a problem? Are we skidding on the ice? The engines are starting to whine. What does that mean? Oh dear God, we're starting to climb into the air. The ground is dropping away below us. I have to close my eyes a minute. That huge clang was the wheels going up. Katie just told me. She's clinging to Jean-François and offered to hold my hand too but I want to write about this, the sheer terror of it.

Hmm, you can get used to it actually. We've been up a while now and I'm growing accustomed to the feel of the airplane. But what a sight out the window!!! I'm not sure if that's Quebec or Labrador below, but it is truly a magnificent winter wonderland down there. Everywhere are hills and dunes of snow and great kings of fir trees laden with frost, and frozen rivers and lakes and so many shades of ice, white and blue and even yellow...

Oh wow, the most amazing thing is happening. Louise started to sing that song the French kids taught us at camp and now everyone is singing it together, as we fly out of our country like the Canada geese.

*Moi, j'ai quitté mon pays bleu,*
*Moi, j'ai quitté mon pays bleu,*
*Moi, j'ai quitté mon pays bleu,*
*Et je n'ai pas su lui dire adieux.*

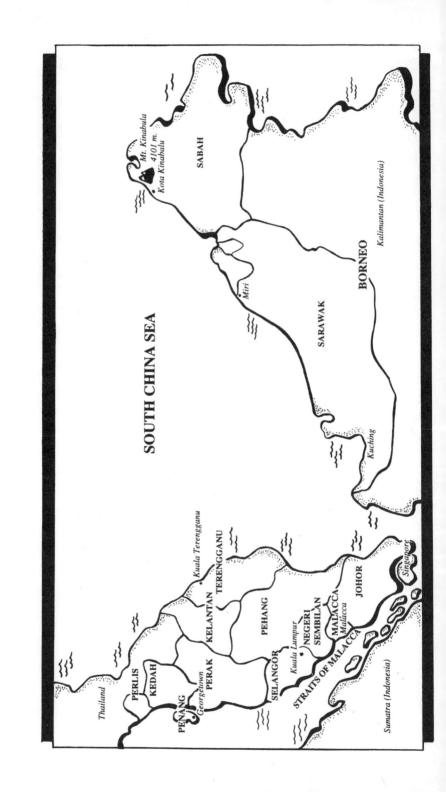

# PART TWO: MALAYSIA

*"Only connect."*

E.M. FORSTER

## January 10, 1972—oops—1973
## Kampung Pandan outside Kuala Lumpur

*I*'m so hot and muggy and tired, I don't feel like writing. I want to take another shower and have another nap. But I mustn't let too much time go by without recording stuff as I might forget what's happening to me and how I feel in these early days.

The first shock is the heat. It's like a blanket that smothers you so that you can hardly move or breathe or even think. Arriving into it after the blizzard in Montreal and the grey drizzle of London, I'm completely spaced out. And then everything else around me. It's all so *different*. I can hardly hold onto the fact that I'm here, let alone take in what I'm looking at. It's a weird sensation, everything seems unreal, like I'm covered in Saran Wrap and can't touch what's outside of me. It makes me feel like I'm not here or I'm only half-here.

I'll start from the beginning, that first sight of Malaysia from the airplane. I thought we were going to crash as we swerved so close to the mountains, nearly touching them with our wings. The Cameron Highlands they're called, must tell Dad. Yet it wasn't Scottish hills I was looking at, but wave after wave of the lushest wettest darkest green imaginable.

We landed at the airport in K.L. That's what everyone calls Kuala Lumpur, a big modern city that looks brand new with its smooth white buildings rising up to the bluest of blue skies. It's not easy to describe the colours here. In the glittering sunlight, each colour is more extreme. Red is redder than red, yellow more yellow.

Everything dazzles so that your eyes hurt.

We were given a fantastic reception, as if we were famous. There were loads of government officials to welcome us and then the press asking questions and taking pictures. It was hilarious to look around at everyone, the kids I mean. We looked so odd, like something out of a time warp, as if we were our parents when they were young, and not from the '70s. Everyone was dressed conservatively, the girls with long skirts or dresses, no micros, no minis, no shorts or hot pants, nothing tight and nothing revealing. The guys wore trousers, no shorts or jeans, with short-sleeved shirts. They all had short hair. (Some of them left it to the very last minute to shave off their beards and moustaches. One by one they went into the bathroom on the plane to come out a while later, hairless as plucked chickens. The rest of us hooted and whistled.)

Except for Marcus's black, Betty's brown and Cyn's light brown, we all looked so *white*, like we were sick. Everyone wore sun-glasses, reinforcing the celebrity impression, and kept wiping the sweat off their faces with handkerchiefs. But it was all smiles and nods and broken conversations in Malay. They kept asking us were we happy to be here. *Ya! Ya!* A thousand times *ya!*

It was great to see Maya and Azahar again. They were obviously delighted to welcome us at last to their country. Strange to see people in their own environment and the difference it makes. Maya seemed to glide through the crowd in her orange sari, like an Indian princess in her court. Azahar was so…masterful I guess the word is. He's obviously an important person here, with assistants running after him and jumping at his command. Both of them seemed bigger or taller now, as if the cold air of Canada had made them more compact, like ice. But in Malaysia, they flowed freely. They spent most of the time talking to Val about our schedules while the rest of us were being assaulted by the horde of journalists. But I managed to get a hug from Maya and a big smile from Azahar—so did 60-odd others!

Then came the bus trip into K.L.: I sat with my face pressed to the window, all eyes and nose and ears, looking, smelling, seeing, hearing. How can I possibly capture all the images that washed over me like the flickering reel of a movie? Crowds of people on the streets, in open-air restaurants, at stalls and in shops. A panorama of different races and cultural dress: white turbans and coloured saris, Malay suits and sarongs, Chinese trousers and tight dresses, and Western clothes as well. The traffic was jammed together in a cloud of exhaust, modern cars and buses alongside trishaws (bicycle rickshaws) and animal carts. Street vendors sat on mats on the sidewalks with trinkets around them and whole streets were markets spilling over with vegetables, fish, flowers and fruits. I tried to drink it all in but really I was drowning in it, overwhelmed by the strangeness of it all.

The bus stopped at a fruit stand so we could sample produce. I had sugar-cane water, very sweet, and rambutans. Yum. They're a kind of white plum with this wild-looking spikey red skin.

I really am too wiped-out to write more. That took a huge effort. No energy left. Must take a nap.

## January 12, 1973

*I* can't believe I've been in Malaysia for four days! I'm still wandering around in a daze, as if all of me didn't arrive when I got here. Parts of me are in London looking at the Tower Bridge, and Dubai being searched for drugs, even though we only had a fifteen-minute break in the airport, or still on the plane over the oil fields of Baghdad. ("This is some *schlepp*," Cyn said to me, somewhere above the continent of India.)

Perhaps I'm jet-lagged. Or maybe it's culture shock. I don't feel like a real person in a real place.

Kampung Pandan is a youth hostel or should I say youth centre. We're staying here for a week while we acclimatize to the weather and food and stuff. The white buildings are like a school compound enclosing a wide green lawn. We are six to a room, in bunks with mosquito nets. At the end of the week, the groups head out to their work projects in different states. I like it here, though it has the feeling of a holding pen, an in-between place. There isn't much to do besides the official receptions we have to attend. Generally we laze around, shower and sleep. I'm too fatigued to get bored or restless, but it leaves me dull and wondering, "Why did I come here?" and "Don't I have better things to do with my life?" Ray bought a stack of English comic books in London—*Beezer*, *Topper* and *Beano*—and we've all been devouring them, as if we were clinging to something familiar.

We go swimming every evening at the public pool. It's specially booked for us so there's no one else there and we don't get to meet anyone. A bus takes us and brings us back again (we're herded around like sheep) but surprise, we can swim with the boys. No bikinis or slinky swim-suits, however, only conservative one-pieces. The guys wear old-fashioned trunks, like shorts. They look so goofy.

My sunburn is killing me. Katie's gloating. She had a really bad one the second day we got here, now she's as brown as her freckles while I'm a boiled lobster. It's my own fault. We were warned about the tropical sun. But it's so awful being pasty white in the middle of summer and surrounded by people who are a lovely coffee colour.

I'm still not eating much and losing weight fast. The food is awful, mostly rice and fish. They put the milk and sugar right into the teapot for tea, ugh. The dessert tonight was little cakes made of something white and mushy like uncooked dough, stuffed with something that looked like crisp brown hair (?!). Couldn't even try it. Sometimes there are egg-salad sandwiches and we all fight to get at them. I would kill for a grilled cheese sandwich or French fries with gravy. Katie says she's dreaming of moose steak and fried cabbage. (To each his own, as Gran would say.) I do eat the fruit, I'm practically on a fruit diet. There are so many kinds and all delicious. Star fruit is pale yellow and shaped like an elongated star. The pineapple is always fresh and crispy. Bananas come in every size and colour, little red ones the size of your hand and then yellow ones the length of your arm! The oranges have a green skin and are much tastier than North American ones. Sweet and sour *langsats* are these little brown guys that have white segments inside, some sweet and some sour. Amazing.

Saw my first giant spider today. Size of my fist. Yikes.

I'm getting used to the tiny lizards that crawl over the

walls and ceilings. Lying in bed last night, I watched a big fight right above me. One ate the tail off the other. I don't worry about them falling on me any more. They seem to have glue on their feet. They eat the mosquitoes, so I look on them as a girl's best friend in Malaysia.

I've had a few chats with our new guy, Dave. He's okay once you get to know him. Kind of shy, with a dry sense of humour, brainy in a different way than Ray or Katie as he's quiet about it and doesn't get involved in discussions. He's actually only 18 but looks about ten years older and acts it too. I thought he was poor, but *both* his parents are professors. No wonder he's so weird. He reads a lot of books, fat ones with small print (who on earth is Proust?). He did not want to read *Go Ask Alice* which is one of the books being passed around since camp. I thought it was terrific. He sniffed and said he never read paperbacks. Katie told him to read James Joyce's *Ulysses* (she lent it to me, forget it) and he said, "I did. Years ago." That took the wind out of her sails, ha ha. I think he's read thousands of books. Carries one with him all the time and starts reading if things get boring, even during receptions and official speeches. He wasn't trained for this programme, so he's just being himself and doesn't care what kind of impression he's making.

There seems to be no end to the official stuff, as various youth groups and government types continue to arrive to welcome us to Malaysia. The only important people we *haven't* met are Tun Abdul Razak, the prime minister, and the Yang di-Pertuan Agong, the king. It's always the same. Hours of speeches, droning on in Malay. Then a long table laid out with pots of sugared tea and inedible treats. Because of the formality and the large numbers involved, we don't really connect with anyone. We had *three* receptions today at 9:30, 11:00 and 2:15. The first two were with government agencies and the last was with the executive of the National Federation of Islamic Youth. That could have been good, since they were young people, but we only had an hour and most of it was taken up with press photographs on the front steps. My face hurts from smiling so much and uttering polite and meaningless phrases. I gave up trying to translate the speeches ages ago, they're delivered so fast, but I know how they start. *Tuan tuan dan puan puan dan belia belia Canada.* I say it in my sleep. Gawd, everything is so planned and formal. When do we get to meet *real* people?

## January 15, 1973

Some of the kids have been smoking dope. This could jeopardize the whole programme. The Malaysian government is totally against drugs, we are talking the death penalty. We could all be sent home in disgrace and the project ended before it even gets going. I could kill those selfish bastards myself. Everyone knows who did it but the question is—do we tell Val? It's all so depressing and confusing. I mean, Katie, Jean-François, Ray and a few others drank a bottle of Scotch in our room tonight. Cyn and Louise were very upset, especially since the guys shouldn't have been in our room in the first place. And isn't that as bad as drugs since it's against the rules too and Muslims are anti-alcohol as well as anti-drugs? Really, I'm too tired and hot to worry about this. I'm fed up with everyone and

81

everything. I'm beginning to regret I ever came on this project. I feel like a caged bird, dying to be set free.

Ah, that reminds me of the beautiful dream I had last night. I was a tiny bird flying over the mountains, my wings spread wide, sailing alone into the wet green landscape of Malaysia.

## January 16, 1973

Not feeling too good tonight. In fact, I haven't felt this bad since I joined the project. Earlier this evening we went to the High Commissioner's house for yet another reception, this time a Canadian one. The only Malaysians present were servants, bringing us drinks and cheese and crackers. We said, "*Terimakaseh,*" to them but it was hardly a situation for practising the language. The other guests were mainly diplomats and big-business people with their families. Not my kind of crowd. Katie said they were so slick if you bumped into them, you'd slide off. The kids were worse than their parents. One guy our age was going on about how bored he was in Malaysia and he complained that he couldn't get near any Malaysian girls. He blamed their religion but when I asked him if he could speak Malay, he said no, of course not, they could speak English if they wanted to. Katie piped up, then, and said that Malaysians were more intuitive than us and maybe the girls could tell he was a jerk just by looking at him. She said it very politely so it took a moment to sink in. I choked on my drink. He went all stiff and said, "Oh yeah?" and walked away. Good one, Katie.

Except for the High Commissioner, who was really nice, I don't think any of the people there could speak Malay. And they acted as if they couldn't see their servants who were just invisible hands giving them things. Constance, who's in Tony's group, enjoyed herself and mingled well. She kept saying this was her idea of life and how marvellous it was. I was disgusted with her, but I guess that comes from growing up in Ottawa.

There was a cloud hanging over everyone when we got back. The whole rich people/government officials/formal stuff is getting us all down. It's like we're trapped in a bubble that keeps us from touching the true heart of Malaysia. We were told to gather in the dining hall where Val announced that some kids are being sent home for taking drugs (only two as it turns out and no one in our group, thank goodness). He said he had no choice as there were some rules that could not be broken without ruining everything. He looked old and tired, and his voice was abrupt. We knew we couldn't argue or ask questions. Then he said he recognized that we were all under a lot of strain but he asked us to be patient and to respect our hosts. The receptions were the government's stamp of approval on our project and the Malaysian way of honouring us. This, too, was part of their culture and an indication of how important they considered us.

In two days, the groups split up for our work projects in different Malaysian states. Will it be more of the same? More receptions and officials? A lot of kids are saying they want to go home. It's not what we expected, not what we imagined. We didn't come here to be ambassadors. I told Katie I was beginning to wonder if I wanted to stay and she said she felt the same way. But we decided we should hang in anyway, who knows what might be around the corner. But, gawd, the whole thing is so depressing.


January 17, 1973

*K*atie, Cyn, Ray and I took a bus into downtown K.L. today. It was a nerve-wracking decision, to forgo the safety of official guides and transport, but we had to do it. It was time to jump in at the deep end and meet the real Malaysia. And guess what? Like all things that are scary because they are unknown, it wasn't half as frightening once we did it. In fact, it was wonderful, walking through the streets like a normal person, mingling with everyday people. We went into Indian flower-shops where they weave long garlands of orchids, and Chinese goldsmiths which also sell jade. The Malay drapers sell bolts of bright batik cloth and rolls of *songket*, material embroidered with gold and silver thread. I bought some glass bangles and a gold chain. Great prices!

We went to the Hilton Hotel for lunch. I felt very guilty. So much for assimilating, but we were starving and can't eat Malaysian food. We stuffed ourselves on hamburgers, French fries, lemonade and ice-cream. That was my first full meal since I got here. The hotel was gorgeous, big and airy, with silverware and linen napkins and flowers on the table. And so cool with the air-conditioning. Sigh.

But that was only a treat, not the best moment. The best was when I heard the Muslim call-to-prayer! It was so unexpected, so magical, I had to stop to take it in. There I was, standing on a modern sidewalk surrounded by tall buildings and offices, and then there it was—a sound ringing out over the city, over the noise and the bustle—a high-pitched call, musical, ancient, beautiful, sacred.

*Allahu Akbar Allahu Akbar*
*Ashadu An La Illa-l-lah*
*Ashadu Anna Muhammadan Rasulu-l-lah*
*Hayya 'Ala-s-salah Hayya 'Ala-s-salah*
*Hayya 'Ala-l-falah Hayya 'Ala-l-falah*
*Allahu Akbar Allahu Akbar*
*La Ilaha Illa-l-lah*

God is the greatest! God is the greatest!
I bear witness that there is no god but God
I bear witness that Muhammed is the Prophet of God!
Come to prayer! Come to prayer!
Come to salvation! Come to salvation!
God is the greatest! God is the greatest!
There is no god but God!

(Azahar wrote this out for me and translated the Arabic. He said the muezzin calls the Believers to prayer five times a day and we heard the midday call.)

I can hardly describe how I felt. It was so different from going into church where you shut out the world and think about God. Here thoughts of God were being sung out into the world, the ordinary world of shopping and crowds and traffic. I finally spotted from where the muezzin was calling, a high tower, overlooking the city. He was too far away to see anything more than a figure but he held a megaphone, I think, in his hands. His voice went right through me, like a thrill.

Katie stopped when I did and we both stood with our heads cocked sideways, listening. When it was over we looked at each other, eyes shining.

"We are in Malaysia," she whispered.

A shiver went up my spine.

That was the moment when I truly landed in this country, body and soul.

January 18, 1973
Kampung Solok Bukit Pulau, Malacca

*F*eels like I'm beginning to settle in at last. Though it was sad and a bit scary saying goodbye to the other groups—safety in numbers—it's the best thing to have happened. We were all shaky and nervous at first but Lise really showed her strength as a group leader, organizing everything, talking to officials and bus drivers, reassuring us, checking that everyone was okay. In fact, it's all so much better really. We're no longer being protected and coddled and muffled away from real life. Now we're part of it!

The first step was that journey out of Kampung Pandan into the countryside, to the state of Malacca. The hot blue sky shimmered over miles and miles of watery rice paddies, irrigation ditches and rubber plantations. Banana trees grew along the roadside, their giant leaves sheltering clusters of yellow fruit. I got a photo of me holding onto a heap of them.

Our new home is great. We're living in a rural *kampung* or village, out in the middle of nowhere, but you can get to

Malacca town by bus. Our house is made of wood and built on stilts a few feet above the ground. (I say for coolness, Darren says for snakes.) The guys' room is on one side, the girls' on the other, with a landing in between which we use as a hallway/lounge. Our bedroom is like a dormitory, long thin beds, side by side, draped with mosquito nets like lace. All you need are sheets and a pillow, it's so warm at night. The kitchen and dining area are separated from the sleeping quarters by a concrete courtyard where there are clay pots for washing clothes and lines for drying. Everything dries in the heat in seconds. We are doing our own shopping and cooking—hurrah! At last we can eat.

The toilets are in a shack in the field behind the house. Squat jobs—you go down on your hunkers—but at least there's toilet paper. (Katie said they still have outhouses in Newfoundland and when her dad built a modern bathroom, her grandfather said, "There'll be no luck when that comes into the house.") The showers are also outside, a bigger shack made of corrugated aluminum, with tiles on the floor.

I saw another giant spider today, hanging there in the middle of a vast web woven between the bushes. The village kids thought it was hilarious that I took a photo of it, as if I had never seen a spider before. We have most of the village hanging around every day, sitting on our front steps, wandering through the house, following us around, watching us cook, eat, wash clothes, even read! It's like living in a huge aquarium and we're the fish, or rather we're some outlandish pale sea creatures with odd habits, ha ha. When we stroll through the *kampung*, people stare at us like we're ghosts. Guess we are, since we're so white. The kids call out, "Hello Joe," (like in Vietnam!) or "*Orang puteh*" (white person). The adults and old people are more formal, though very friendly, smiling and nodding at us and waving us inside their houses for *kopi* or *teh*.

The houses are dotted higgledy-piggledy, shaded by palm trees, on grass or rough ground. (There are no sidewalks as we're out in the sticks.) All are built on stilts and made of wood, with brightly coloured curtains blowing in the windows and shutters painted in pale pinks and blues. Many have carvings on the walls and the edges of the roof. Sometimes the steps leading up to the front door are painted too, with designs like mosaics. You always leave your shoes on the steps before you go into a house.

I'm sitting here on our front steps. The sun is beating down on the page and I can smell the warm paper. Directly before me are flat green paddy fields criss-crossed with irrigation ditches. In the distance rise high green mountains. Everywhere palm trees waver in the hot breeze. A little girl of about ten just passed by, herding two huge water buffalo. The patties they leave behind are *ginormous*. Darren stepped in one yesterday to Cyn and Katie's delight. There are always animals around, even when you go to town; water buffalo, monkeys, chickens, goats, geese, and cows like the sacred ones in India. There goes the call for supper. Rice and vegetables in soya sauce (I peeked). Dave has gone vegetarian. Smells yum.

January 19, 1973

*M*y hands are shaking. No, the writing's steady. Maybe I'm only trembling on the inside. I'll try to describe what happened. Mr. and Mrs. Vasu, two of our resource people in Malacca, took us to a Hindu temple for the festival of Thai Pusam. The temple was beautiful, all white with steps leading up to it and pillars set far apart so that it was open to the air. The altar was golden, with statues of many-armed gods and goddesses who seemed to be dancing. There were clouds of incense, and garlands of flowers everywhere, orchids of vivid red, purple, yellow and orange, on the altar, on the floor, around the pillars, entwined in the long braids of the women and draped on the shoulders of the men. We wore them too. First there was a ritual cleansing of the statues, nine times, with water, incense and perfumed oils. Musicians played on stringed instruments and drums, a rhythmic beat that stirred the blood. Then a procession arrived and everyone gathered outside the temple to welcome them. Silken banners and tasselled canopies shone in the sunlight. There were more musicians in the parade and people of every age from children to the very old. Suddenly I saw them.

Can words tell? There were people with metal skewers piercing their cheeks and tongues, and hooks in their backs that pulled at their skin. One man carried a kind of cage over him made of long sharp needles that pricked every inch of his back, neck, chest and stomach. The men were thin and wiry, some quite old, and there were women too, with needles in their tongues and noses and cheeks. All appeared to be in a trance, with glazed eyes that gazed inward. Some danced and twirled around, quivering with metal quills that glinted in the sunshine. One skinny old man charged right up to me and shook his head wildly. The long skewer that ran through his cheeks bounced up and down. I nearly died, but managed not to scream. When he danced away, the Indians near me laughed.

With the music and the hot sun and everyone dressed in clothes that sparkled, it was like a sacred Mardi Gras. It was definitely a celebration, all smiles and laughter, even though Mrs. Vasu explained that those who had pierced themselves did so to atone for their sins or the sins of their family. They danced around for ages, then stood on the temple steps where the priests pulled out the skewers and pins and hooks and needles. *No blood!!!* Some people fainted, however, and were laid out on blankets and fanned back to consciousness.

I've never seen anything like it in my life. I tried to imagine Reverend Merry witnessing this and couldn't. When I think of our form of worship, everyone in dark colours in a plain setting, singing hymns in a quiet and orderly manner, it blows my mind how human beings can be so *different.*

And yet, though I felt in some ways like a visitor to another planet, somehow, somewhere inside me, I was connected to it. I wore flowers too. I swayed in time with the music. And the Indian onlookers themselves seemed as awed as I was. We were all human beings together amazed by the mystery, the power of unseen forces, belief over pain, mind over matter.

I can't write much more. I'm still trembling inside, somewhere in my soul. The other kids were affected too. We're all quiet this evening. Some have gone on walks by themselves, others are sitting alone like me, writing or just thinking. Should I say it? But it will sound too weird or Holy Joe. Oh what the heck, no one's going to read this anyway. Okay I'll just write the truth of it.

God was there in that temple.

90

January 24, 1973

*W*e had the official opening of our work project four days ago—*tuan tuan dan puan puan dan belia belia Canada*—and so far so good. We work in the mornings, the coolest time of day, and the afternoons are free if there aren't planned outings or receptions. Our job is to clear the *belukar*, secondary jungle, from the fields in the back of the house. It's common land belonging to the *kampung*, and we're clearing it for the villagers to plant crops. We use *parangs*, Malaysian machetes which are curved like a sickle. Several youth groups are involved in the project: Boy Scouts, Girl Guides, the village youth brigade and an Islamic youth group.

It's much easier mixing with other kids when you work side by side and take breaks together. Trouble is they want to practise English and we want to speak Malay, so the conversations are pretty disjointed. One girl asked me how I liked "the horse" and I tried to explain in Malay that we didn't keep animals. She kept shaking her head and saying, "No, no, *horse*," and after some sign language and pointing, I finally understood. She meant "house." I wasn't going to insult her by laughing, but when she realized her mistake she went into a fit of giggles and called her friends over to tell them what she had done (all in fast Malay). They fell around the place. I guess Malaysians aren't embarrassed by mistakes the way we are, or maybe they just love laughing. Whenever the youth groups work with us, there is always a tremendous amount of giggling and laughing going on. It's unnerving sometimes, because even as they don't mind laughing at themselves they also feel free to laugh at us. From what I can tell, they think we're hilarious.

January 27, 1973

*K*atie and I have made friends with a *kampung* woman, Rohani. She gave us sarongs, long skirts made with gorgeous batik patterns. Mine is deep blue with green and yellow birds. Katie's is yellow with pink and purple flowers. Rohani showed us how to wear them, tightly wrapped around you and tucked in at the waist. They're really comfortable and cool and they make you walk slower because of the tightness, and also the possibility that the tuck might come undone and down goes your skirt! I wear mine with a T-shirt, but I want to buy some of the fitted blouses that normally go with them, made of lace or sparkly material. The three of us have planned a shopping spree in town this weekend. I want a *baju kurong* as well, the long, flowing national dress of the Muslim women. It has a voluminous skirt that you pleat at the waist so it drapes in loose folds to the ground. Over that goes a long shirt made of the same material as the skirt, which hangs to the knee. *Baju kurongs* are light and silky, whereas sarongs are made of cotton.

Rohani is going to teach us how to haggle when we shop. She says you never pay the marked price or the first price offered by the vendor as that's merely the starting point for bargaining. Of course we didn't know this. Rohani grinned, "They see you and say, 'Oh good, here comes money.'"

Rohani doesn't know a lot of English but Katie speaks to her in Malay and I do my best. The whole language thing is an experience in itself. When you can't rely on words, you have to fall back on facial expressions, intuition and anything else you can use to understand and to communicate.

In some ways, it's more direct, more sincere. You pay more attention to *who* the person is, not what they are saying. There was something about Rohani that clicked right away. I just knew that she was my kind of person. (It works in the reverse too. You know immediately if you don't like someone. You can see things in a person's face that you wouldn't normally see when you're busy listening to their words— like if they are open or closed to friendship or if they are happy with their life, or angry and resentful.)

We visit Rohani every day after work. Though she's only 19, she's married, with a gorgeous pudgy little baby. Her husband, Mokhtar, works in the agricultural ministry. He told us the other day to boil all our water in case of typhoid. Yikes! He's a real cutie, like a young Omar Sharif. We watched television at their house last night, black and white with terrible reception. First "Mannix" with Malay subtitles and then a Malay comedy-horror-musical, no subtitles. What a hoot. Rohani and Mokhtar and a few neighbours kept laughing and getting all excited as they explained what was going on, plus Katie trying to translate though she was barely following the plot, and everyone in stitches. We had *kopi* and black rice porridge for a snack, delicious. Didn't get to bed till midnight.

January 29, 1973

*I* was tired all day after a restless night. Sometimes it's hard to get to sleep with all the noises from the frogs, cicadas and who knows what else that are under the house. They must be gigantic, or else they have microphones down there. They sound like enormous elastic bands going "twoingg twoingg"—no—"TWOINGG TWOINGG" accompanied by an incredible range of burps and squeaks and squawks. The bugs are HUGE here. Five-inch spiders and giant bees, millipedes and centipedes and all kinds of other weird-legged things. Ugh.

Cyn hacked Katie's arm at work today, by accident of course. Scared the wits out of everyone as the blood poured down from a big gash. Katie swore like a trooper and ran over to Darren. He went white as a sheet and told her to find Lise (big help). I grabbed her arm and put pressure on it as we raced for the house. Lise got out the first-aid kit to clean and bandage it, then drove her to the hospital. Tetanus shot and three stitches! Katie says she hopes there will be a scar so she can show off her "wound from South-East Asia." What a kid.

After work we all went to the beach. Wow, swimming in the Straits of Malacca, a dream come true. The water was the clearest aquamarine and warm like a bath. You could see the white sand bars below and sea cucumbers and all kinds of exotic plants and fish. Got stung by a jelly-fish! Ouch. Ray, too. Those blobs of jelly look harmless till they get you. It was wonderful sun-bathing under the palm trees on hot silvery sand. I felt like the idle rich.

Katie and I went for a long walk and had one of our heart-to-hearts. It's been a while. The days are so full of work and meeting people and experiencing new things that we usually fall into bed at night exhausted. No time for chats. We talked about our families and our childhood. She remembers being hungry a lot and dreaming about food, especially fruit and desserts. She wants to go to university, to be a professor, or maybe go into politics or law. She could get a scholarship as she's top of her class but she has to go to work, like her older brothers and sisters, to bring in money for the family. I couldn't imagine her working in a canning factory or anything like that, it seems so unfair. She got very depressed talking about it. When I told her I hoped to get into the journalism programme at Carleton, she was very excited and said I was to stick to my plan and not settle for anything less than my dream. I've always taken for granted that I would go to university. I know I'll have to work part-time and Mom and Dad will scrimp and save to help me, but there's no question of me *not* going because of money. It must be so much harder to plan your life when you don't have anything to back you up and if you have other responsibilities like your family.

Katie also talked about Jean-François and how much she misses him. She says he'll always be special because he was her first lover, but she doesn't think she's in love with him, because she doesn't know the real him. It's the language barrier again. His English isn't that great and her French is nothing to write home about. They don't have deep discussions about anything, it's all kidding around and playing together, "puppy love" she calls it. She didn't know he was intellectual till she saw him talking one day with a bunch of the French kids. They were discussing the FLQ and separatism, and Jean-François was holding the floor with streams of words and a deadly serious face. Then he raised his fist and cried, "*Vive le Québec libre!*" like Charles de Gaulle. When Katie saw him like that, so fierce and intelligent, she was crushed. She realized he was someone she didn't know at all, even as she was only one small part of herself with him. *C'est triste.*

Then she confided in me that she's getting a strange kind of crush on Darren! That freaked me out completely. I know he's attracted to her, but I thought she couldn't stand him. She's always fighting with him over his background. She went nuts when she caught him reading Ayn Rand the other day (*Atlas Shrugged*) and said that every rich kid read "that simplistic fascist bullshit" to convince themselves they were the cream of society by merit instead of by birth. That was some fight. She roared at him. "You think cream rises to the top in our country? Well, I say society is a septic tank. You know what rises to the top in a septic tank? PURE SHIT."

She really ought to go into politics. She would put the House of Commons on its head.

I reminded her of these arguments and other stuff she has said about Darren—I mean, he drives her mental sometimes—and I said I thought he would be very bad for her head. She sighed and said, "Yeah, I know. But he's so cute." Had to laugh.

That's when I got up the nerve to tell her about Ray and me and our near-miss as a couple. She said she suspected something, what with all the wrestling. I didn't tell her the private stuff about Ray's family, I wouldn't break my promise to him, not even with my best friend, but I said I felt he would be too much to take on right now.

Actually, it's been okay with him and me ever since the airport. We still kid around a lot. The other night, he hid behind the kitchen door when I was cooking and jumped out suddenly with that monster routine of his. Scared the dickens out of me. I screeched blue murder.

## January 30, 1973

*M*ail from home at last! It sure takes a long time to get here, but then it goes to Val in K.L. first and he reroutes it. Dad is improving day by day though he hates being cooped up in the house with mainly Gran for company. He wants to get back to work but Mom put her foot down. She's running the shop with Matt and Daniel's help, all of them doing their best to ignore Dad's interference (I can just imagine). Mom says she's enjoying bragging about me to her friends though she's still dazed at the thought of her "little girl" in Asia. Seems they haven't got any of my letters yet. I've sent three *Surat Udara* aerogrammes, only 30 cents apiece, which are sheets of thin blue paper that fold up into an airmail envelope.

It was my turn again in the kitchen today. I forgot to mention my first time, total disaster. I thought I should boil the lettuce in case of cholera. Yuk. I only had to worry about supper this time (everyone gets their own breakfast) as we were invited to a wedding in another *kampung* about seven miles away. It's considered good luck to have "Europeans" attend, not that you would have noticed the extra people in the crowd. It was a huge affair, over 1,500 guests. Three sittings for the feast. The bride and groom were dressed in silver clothes and they sat on ceremonial chairs for hours, like statues, while the rest of us stuffed ourselves and watched a display of dancing and *silat*, the Malay art of self-defence. The food was fantastic, *nasi beriani* (festival rice), piles of satay, curried beef and chicken, *beehun* and *meehun goreng* (fried noodle dishes) and all kinds of scrumptious desserts. The tables and chairs were set up outdoors. We met loads of people. They were all surprised that we were living in a *kampung* instead of staying in hotels.

I made a light supper when we got back as we had all pigged out at the wedding. Gave them salads and little egg pancakes that Rohani taught me how to cook. Later, a gang of us went to meet some of the youth-group workers at 49 Stalls in Malacca town, the open-air *restoran* on the wharfs. It's a great place, with loads of stalls offering all kinds of fast food, Malaysian-style, satay, fried oysters, fish and shellfish of every kind, fried noodles and rice, and a hundred other Chinese, Malay and Indian snacks. Have to laugh when I remember how much we hated the food at first. I mean, we can't get enough of it now. And while the guys are getting thinner and thinner no matter how much they eat, us girls are increasing at an alarming rate! Must be the difference between male and female metabolisms.

Katie drank beer in public which surprised me, but she said she couldn't stay dry any longer. The Malaysians didn't look too bothered about it. In fact they were surprised that most of us refrained. None of the Muslim kids had alcohol while the Chinese guys drank only a bottle or two of beer, but Ray was really knocking them back. Katie had three beers but she told Darren she was dying to get drunk and felt she couldn't do it in front of our co-workers. So the two of them went off to drink in a brothel! (Don't ask me how Darren knew where the brothel was, but the fact is he did.) I figured Katie was trying to get him alone. She's such a good actress, you would never guess she was interested in him as she kept making sarcastic remarks in his direction. But you know what, I think he enjoys it. Or maybe she did need to get drunk? But she's too young to be an alcoholic, isn't she?

Cyn and I left the *restoran* earlier than the others and took the bus home. She had been talking with one of the youth-group leaders, Yusuf, all evening and they had arranged to meet back at our house. He offered to take her on his motorbike but she felt it wouldn't look right. I decided to go with her, as Ray was getting tipsy and starting to mess with my hair. I didn't want any public scenes. Cyn talked about Yusuf all the way home so I knew something was up. He's a schoolteacher as well as a youth leader, 21 years old, and very handsome. Dark eyes and a moustache.

When we got back, we found Claude and Louise in the kitchen having cups of tea by candlelight. Yusuf had already arrived and was sitting with them, so we joined the party. We had a deep discussion about religion. Yusuf got quite impassioned. He said the West accepted Eastern religions like Buddhism and Hinduism because we don't feel threatened by them, since they are passive not active. But Islam is assertive like Christianity, with missionaries and the same belief in itself as the one true faith. I always thought of Christianity as a tolerant religion, but didn't know that Islam recognized Jesus as a great prophet, while Christians don't honour Muhammed and know little or nothing about him.

Every time Yusuf mentioned Christianity he looked at Cyn as if he expected her to say something, but though Claude and Louise and I were talking, Cyn kept quiet. (She told me once she doesn't like discussing religion any more than politics, but she agrees with Irving Layton that "Xtianity" is the greatest persecutor of the Jews.) Yusuf

99

seemed perplexed by the fact that she obviously didn't feel included in the discussion and he finally asked her outright if she was Christian.

"No," she said, after hesitating a moment.

"I thought you might be an Arab," he said softly. His voice was like a caress.

"I'm not," she said, just as softly. "I'm a Jew."

Well, to give him credit, he recovered very quickly, though his eyes were huge.

"And you have come to an Islamic country?"

Now I have to admit, I was really glad he asked, because I've been dying to ask Cyn this question ever since camp, but I didn't want to pry or be insensitive. I figured she'd talk about it when and if she wanted to. I leaned forward to hear her answer even as Claude, Louise and Yusuf did. We were like a sacred circle, heads bent together in the candlelight.

Cyn shrugged and smiled a little and her face was so beautiful, that smooth skin even browner now from the Malaysian sun and those dark eyes with long lashes and her shining black hair. No wonder Yusuf thought she was an Arab girl.

"I've come for myself and no one else. My parents have no time for hands-across-the-border. They say it results in dead Jews. They could be right. History says they are. But I wanted to go beyond history, beyond politics, to see what it would be like. What you would be like. I read the Sufi poets. I love what Rumi says. *Beyond the world of right-doings and wrong-doings, there is a field. I will meet you there.*"

It was obvious that Yusuf was attracted to Cyn before she spoke, but it was even more obvious that he was in love with her by the time she was finished. Neither of them talked much after that, though they kept staring at each other, long meaningful looks, while the rest of us chatted away pretending we didn't notice. It was like watching a tale from the Arabian Nights unfold. Not that they were doing anything, I mean, they weren't even sitting together. But you could sense it somehow, like perfume in the air. Something bright hovered over them, an echo of the Garden of Delights that Yusuf had been describing earlier. When it was time for him to go, Cyn walked him to the door and you could hear their voices murmuring in the hallway, then he was gone.

Louise and Claude and I were straining to hear what they said (we're all so nosy), but thankfully Cyn came back to tell us they're going to the movies tomorrow. She talked with us for a while about feeling confused as she doesn't know if she should date him or not. Is it against the rules? Nothing was said about this kind of thing in the training camps, though come to think of it, it was bound to happen, wasn't it? Yusuf isn't sure he should be seeing her either since he's part of the Malaysian side of the programme. For all their worrying, I notice they've made their arrangements anyway. Romeo and Juliet in South-East Asia. Sigh.

I joked with Cyn. "You're the last person I expected to create an international incident on the project."

She just smiled, from somewhere else entirely. The Garden of Delights, ha ha.

It's funny, but the general social situation with its hands-off restrictions, where no one gets to paw each other or neck or pet (let alone have sex), makes it all more romantic.

And from the sublime to the ridiculous! Darren and

Katie came home at about 2:00 a.m. this morning, drunk out of their skulls, talking at the top of their lungs, giggling and "ssshing" all over the place, plus a lot of disgusting slurping noises which I will question Katie about if and when I ever speak to her again. I'm really pissed off with her because she's the one who's always complaining about others being insensitive, turning on the lights and making noise, etc., when she's trying to sleep. I gave her the silent treatment today but she was so hung-over she didn't notice. She spent the day in bed.

February 3, 1973

Chinese New Year's Eve
Today we split up to be adopted into Chinese families for the New Year's celebrations. Hurrah, Katie and I are in the same family. Our sister, Mei-ping, is 16. She came to pick us up with her older brother, Benny, and her sister, Sandra. They all have the same father but different mothers. Mr. Lee is a wealthy businessman who has three wives and loads of kids. Benny is the eldest, "number one son," at 22 years old. His mother's the first wife. (All the kids hang out together but the wives live in separate houses.) Mei-ping's mother is number three wife and we are staying in her house. Sandra's mother is number two wife. Number one house is the biggest, with servants and loads of rooms, an old-style Chinese mansion with huge ornaments and vases and lacquered screens. Benny's mother was playing mah-jong with her friends and didn't come out to meet us, but his dad sat with us for a while. Mr. Lee was friendly

and easygoing, asked us questions about ourselves and the project. He's obviously a man of the world and has been to Canada several times on business.

We sat on the veranda where a servant brought us a delicious noodle-and-pork dish which we ate with chopsticks. There were plants and exotic flowers everywhere and a big fan overhead cooling the air. Then Benny drove us to Mei-ping's house. It's smaller but very pretty, with the same kind of ornaments, screens, lacquer cabinets and carved tables with glass tops.

Mei-ping's mom is young, in her late twenties I'd say, and very beautiful, but she seemed quiet and kind of sad. I guess it was an arranged marriage. We were warned not to ask about such things, but sometimes poor families marry off their daughters to rich businessmen. It's obviously okay for the kids, as Mei-ping loves her dad, visits him and her brothers and sisters all the time, and she'll be going to university when she's finished school.

Mei-ping's mom wore a red silk Chinese dress with embroidery all over it and golden buttons. Her hair was cut short, in black curls, and she wore make-up and dangly earrings. She sat in the living room waiting for Mei-ping's father to collect her. He comes once a week to take her out and he stays the night. The rest of the week she lives by herself with Mei-Ping. It must be lonely for a young woman. We could tell she didn't really want to talk to us, so we didn't bother her. When she was gone, the house seemed lighter somehow and Mei-ping got into the spirit of things. She lent Katie a dark-green dress, tight-fitting in the Chinese style, but she had to go next door to borrow something for me. (I have a feeling her neighbour's plump.

I must stop stuffing myself on Malaysian food!) As midnight approached, we headed off to meet Benny at a Buddhist temple to ring in the New Year.

*KONG HEY FAT CHOY!*

Gongs rang loudly into the night. The front of the temple was open to the street. The inside sparkled like a dragon's treasure-trove, with painted statues draped in red and gold. The air was perfumed with the scent of incense from giant joss sticks about five feet high and three inches thick. People waved bunches of long thin incense sticks over their heads. We set off firecrackers on the sidewalk. A man knelt near a side altar and cast wooden pegs on the ground to tell his fortune. Drums were beaten to accompany the gongs while people chanted. They prayed in Mandarin, I think, though a lot of people speak Hokkien as well, like Mei-ping, if their families originated from Fukien Province in China. Benny walked up to the centre altar and placed bowls of flowers, rice, fruit and tiny ritual cakes there. Around these he burned golden paper folded into the shape of sampans, Chinese boats. These were symbols of the richness of the earth and his family's hope for health and prosperity in the new year.

The temple was Taoist as well as Buddhist, with statues of many different gods and goddesses of war, wind and sea. Some of them looked like fierce warriors, others didn't look human at all. And of course there were statues of the Buddha as well, whom I recognized. He's always smiling. I like that, it makes me smile back. Imagine, before this project I'd never even been in a Roman Church and here I've been to a Hindu and a Buddhist temple!

*KUNG SI FATT CHAI!* (Hokkien)

104

## February 3, 1973

*U*p early, sweet buns and Chinese tea for breakfast before we visited Mei-ping's grandparents. It's the tradition to visit your relatives in the first two days of New Year's (which goes on for fifteen days!) and you start with the elders first. Mei-ping's granny wore a silk "pyjama" trouser suit and was really sweet. We kept bowing and smiling and shaking hands. She gave each of us an *ang pow,* a red envelope with golden writing which had money inside. (That's traditional too, the kids get money in *ang pows* for New Year's. I like it!) She also offered us "love letters," crispy rolled-up wafers stamped with Chinese characters, and other yummy cakes, candies and nuts. Dishes of goodies were set out on black lacquered tables since open-house is held throughout the holiday.

When we went back to Mei-ping's, I had to have a nap, as I was feeling sick. Diarrhea again! I could hear visitors coming and going downstairs, voices talking in Chinese a mile a minute, and the ivory click-clack of mah-jong tiles. I was reminded of Christmas at our house, all the aunts and uncles and neighbours dropping by, and I was sad I couldn't join them. Got up at 7:00 p.m. for dinner and ate pig's intestines without knowing it. Tasted good! I haven't eaten much pork here, as the Muslim Malays don't eat it, but it's the favourite meat of the Chinese. Benny came over and drove us to Sandra's and the gang of us went to the waterfront stalls for pork buns and noodles. Yum.

When we got back, Mei-ping's mother gave us *ang pows.* She looked much happier today after entertaining her guests. She had changed into casual clothes, slacks and a

105

sweater, and was relaxing in an armchair with her feet tucked under her. She asked us questions about the Chinese in Canada and how they lived. Like an idiot, all I could talk about was Chinese restaurants and Chinatowns. Finally I had to admit I didn't know much about them, nor did Katie. We mentioned Jenny, the group leader. Mei-ping's mom was surprised to hear that she wasn't married. We couldn't even tell her if Chinese-Canadian men had more than one wife, though we thought not as bigamy is illegal in Canada (I think).

This wasn't the first time I was forced to realize how little I know about other groups in Canada besides my own. How have I managed to live so long and not know anything about my country? I could tell her history and geography and politics and stuff, but why don't we learn more about *our people*?

## February 5, 1973

Katie and I didn't want to leave Mei-ping's today, but we suddenly remembered that we had volunteered to be the cooks for our farewell party to which we had invited all our friends in Malacca! We told Mei-ping, Sandra and Benny to come (what's three more?) then set off home by bus to our *kampung*. Total disaster met us there! The whole kitchen reeked like a dead body. We opened the fridge to find ten chickens crawling with flies and stinking to high heaven. Someone had turned off the refrigerator when we left for our Chinese families! Oodles of guests due that evening, the feast destroyed and no food in the house. PANIC.

We ran to get a bus to the market. Luckily Dr. Wong was just driving up to bring Dave and Darren back from his house. He dropped them off and drove us downtown where we bought four *katils* of prawns, a pile of orange and pink angel fish, three dozen eggs, and heaps of fruits and vegetables. It was a good thing Dr. Wong showed up, as the markets were closing early for New Year's, plus he bargained for us so we got lots more stuff than usual with the grocery money. Then he drove us back to the *kampung* again, what a sweetie, so we invited him and his family to the party too.

Back at the house, the others were arriving home from their Chinese families. We shooed them out of the kitchen, told them to clean up the place and to hang streamers and balloons in the hall. First we had to wash out the fridge. Out went the ten maggoty chickens. Gross! Lots of screams, but we got the guys to do that. Then we mopped down the kitchen and burned incense to cover up the stink.

At last we could start cooking. We spent the whole afternoon over the stove. Katie made a curried potato dish and *nasi goreng* (fried rice). I decided to go for broke and cook the two fancy dishes Rohani taught us—*laksa*, noodles in fish curry with raw vegetables, and *rojak*, a kind of hot salad made with prawn fritters, shredded cucumber and bean sprouts, topped with a spicy peanut sauce. (Claude pronounced them "*parfait.*" Maybe I'll be a chef instead of a journalist?) For a fruit extravaganza, we sliced up papayas, guavas, mangos and mangosteens and arranged them around a pomelo, a giant citrus fruit the size of a basketball. And last but not least, we whipped up hundreds of little egg pancakes with onions, Malay-style. We were barely finished, showered and changed when the first guests walked in.

107

Mr. and Mrs. Vasu, who had taken us to the Hindu temple, came with their two sons. Cyn had invited Yusuf (natch) and he arrived with a gang of kids from the youth groups who had worked with us. Rohani and Mokhtar came and other villagers who were friends of the group. Benny, Mei-ping and Sandra drove up, as did Dr. Wong and family. (He said he had to see the results of our work, ha ha.) Definitely a big crowd! We placed chairs along the walls in the kitchen and the hallway. The food was laid out on the table, buffet-style. There was a jar filled with orchids for a centre-piece as well as lighted candles. It looked fantastic!

The meal was a great success. And it felt so good to be giving something back to the people who had given so much to us. The whole evening was magical, everyone talking and laughing about the times we had shared together, all the different languages floating out into the night air—French, English, Malay, Chinese, Tamil. It was as if the whole world was gathered in that little house, having a party.

February 6, 1973

We leave Malacca tomorrow! I can't believe it. Our first work project has ended. *Time is fleeting and the bird is on the wing.* (Cyn lent me two of her Sufi books to read, *The Rubaiyat of Omar Khayyam*, and Idries Shah's *Tales of the Dervishes.* I'd heard of Sufis before, but I didn't know they were Muslim. Wonderful stories.)

The whole morning was spent cleaning up the house and packing. The afternoon was free to say goodbye to all our friends in the *kampung*. The worst was Rohani. Katie and I went together. The three of us started bawling but that made the baby cry so we had to stop. We've promised to write, but it's so painful knowing that we won't be back here again. I hadn't thought about this part of the project. Getting close to people you'll never see again. It's hard.

I am excited about moving on, though. Next stop, Terengganu, on the east coast. Who knows what adventures and experiences lie in wait for us there? But at the same time, I'm sad to be leaving behind familiar places and people. We were happily settled here. Everything got so easy, shopping in the market, working with other youth groups, wandering around the *kampung* and visiting our neighbours, meeting friends in town for a night out at the stalls...

Got to go. Lise has called a meeting in the kitchen to discuss our travel plans for tomorrow. Apparently we're staying one night at Val's in K.L. It'll be nice to see him again.

## February 7, 1973

Our departure from Solok Bukit Pulau was very moving. The whole village turned out. The women came up to me and the other girls to give us that beautiful Malay handshake, cupping our hands and touching their hearts. The men shook hands with the men of course. Everyone seemed to be bowing to each other, like in a dance. A dance of affection and farewell...

I was about to get on the mini-bus that was taking us into town when Benny drove up with Mei-ping and

Sandra. More hugs and goodbyes, but then Benny offered to take me and Katie in his car to the bus station, so off we drove. I don't know how to explain this. How I suddenly realized that I belonged in Malaysia now. Saying farewell to the village was like leaving home in Calabogie. (The neighbours came to wish me luck in the "Far East.") Then Meiping driving up was like Shirley and her gang coming to get me for a weekend at her parents' cottage. I mean, it was all so natural. The fact that I was surrounded by palm trees, houses on stilts and people who were speaking Malay and Chinese seemed less exotic somehow. It was the feeling between us that mattered, and the feelings were familiar; love and friendship, family and belonging.

In Malacca town, before I got on the bus for K.L., Benny asked me if I thought we could meet again before I went back to Canada. I'm embarrassed to admit this, but I stared at him blankly for a minute and then realized he was interested in me. I got flustered and went red and couldn't think of what to say. He gave me a funny look, like he was weighing me up, and then he asked straight out.

"Maybe you wouldn't date a Chinese boy?"

Like, who's he kidding? This guy could give handsome lessons and on top of that he's intelligent, charming and let's not forget rich. I've never been so flattered in my life. (This project is doing wonders for my self-esteem.) I'm glad he asked though, since it helped me to get my act together. I told him quite honestly it was his age, that I never thought anyone in their twenties would ask me out. He was surprised when I told him I was only 17—he thought I was 20!—and then he looked a little embarrassed himself. We ended up laughing about it and exchanging addresses.

There were a few raised eyebrows when I got on the bus. My group is so nosy and everyone jumping to conclusions as usual. Even Cyn gave me a special little smile. Yusuf had brought her to the station on his motorbike. He stood on the platform and waved to her as the bus pulled out. She looked sad and kept waving back till he was out of sight.

We arrived in K.L. at noon and took *teksis* straight here, to Val's place, on Jalan Yap Kawn Seng. It's a modern apartment in a high-rise, white walls inside and out, with Western-looking furniture—sofa, armchairs, coffee table, television. The kitchenette has a freezer with loads of fast food in it, hamburgers and the like. We had fun kidding Val about "not connecting." He was suitably sheepish but said he's a hopeless cook and though he eats out in Malaysian he can only look after himself in Western. After a lot of ribbing, we let it go, ha ha. The place is pretty messy as it's his office as well. He has a big typewriter and a photocopier and there are boxes of envelopes and papers everywhere.

It was great to see kids from the other groups. They were leaving as we arrived. We're all in transit right now, changing projects and travelling to different states. Two of the girls, Claire and Maggie, didn't move on. They're waiting for a flight back to Canada! What a bummer. They don't want to finish the programme. They seem really different somehow. I can't put my finger on it, but I found I couldn't talk to them. (Maybe it's me who's changed and the problem is they haven't?) They seem so closed-off or something, like they don't want to let anything reach them. I tried to ask how their work project went—in Terengganu, the state we're heading for tomorrow—but they just shrugged and clammed up. Was everything too different for them?

111

I'm beginning to wonder if the group leaders don't make a big difference. Lise helped me through some hard stuff and I know she had long talks with the others too. She was always calling meetings to air grievances and more importantly to get out people's fears and doubts about what we were doing. Maybe Claire and Maggie's group leaders didn't help them when they needed it? Maybe they felt too alone facing the new?

I guess I'll never know because no one's talking. That pisses me off. How can you learn from other people's mistakes if everyone shuts up when something goes wrong?

I'm sitting on Val's balcony as I write this, watching the sun set over the city. It's a warm breezy evening. I can hear a muezzin calling from a minaret nearby. *Come to prayer. Come to prayer...*

Dear God, please help me to be strong enough for this project. To be open to learn. Help me to do what I have come here to do and let me do it with joy in my heart.

February 8, 1973
Jalan Gong Tok Nasek, Kuala Terengganu

O ur new home is a big wooden shop-house painted silver, no stilts. We're on a paved street in the middle of town—K.T. as they call Kuala Terengganu—with lots of houses around and behind us. The house has two floors and loads of rooms. The top floor has six bedrooms which we've divided among us. The girls decided right off to give Lise her own room as she has paperwork to do at night and we knew she would appreciate the private space. But the guys had a huge argument over who had to share with whom, as there were four of them and only three rooms. What a meeting that was. The girls sat back and watched the fur fly!

Neither Dave nor Ray nor Darren wanted to share with each other, but all felt they could handle sharing with Claude. However, it was the first time I saw Claude refuse to budge or compromise. He kept insisting, in French and English, that he was the eldest and should have his own room. Of course it was obvious that he wanted his own room so Louise could sneak in at night, but the guys were being either stupid or stubborn because they refused to give it to him. In the end they demanded that names be drawn from a hat. Lise sighed and shrugged at Louise, but agreed this was the fairest way. Hurrah! Claude got his own room, Dave, too, and Ray has to share with Darren. (Neither looked too happy about it.)

I'm lying on my bed, looking out the window straight up at a coconut tree. The huge palms wave like arms against a dazzling blue sky. I'm sharing with Katie (of course). Tomorrow we are to meet a federation of *seberkas* or national youth groups. They're members of the National Federation of Islamic Youth and we've been told to dress conservatively. We're all going out for supper tonight, to have a look at K.T. It's smaller than Malacca but busy all the same. It's a nice change to be back in town.

February 9, 1973

*On the shore beside the tropical sea*
*You will stand to welcome me*

*On the shore beneath the sky so blue.*

*I*'m almost afraid to put it down on paper. I know already that words won't do justice to my feelings, to what has happened, to what is happening. They will make it sound stupid or ridiculous or unbelievable. I can't possibly describe how deep these feelings are because they come from a place where words have never been and they go to a place that words can't reach. But I'm going to try anyway. (Like a crow that insists on singing despite the squawks.)

His name is Ahmed. (My heart beats quicker just whispering those two syllables. I feel as if I've been running too fast.) He was there at the reception. Oh, it's all so strange. To try and remember how I felt before I knew he existed.

I was there in the big hall, sitting on a chair in the front row between Katie and Louise. Behind us were rows and rows of Malay youth groups who had been bussed in from all over the place. The chairs had been set up facing a dais which held the chief leaders of Islamic Malay youth. I was happy to see many girls included, most of them dressed in *baju kurongs* with kerchiefs on their heads. It was so different from the usual official function where the speeches were made by government representatives all well over the age of 30. At last, a true *youth* reception!

For a change I wasn't day-dreaming, nor did I have to keep giving Katie a dig to stop her from sleeping on my shoulder. Even Dave left his book in his shoulder bag. As each leader spoke, they talked directly to us as their peers, talked about their own youth groups, what they hoped to achieve, how they furthered the hopes and dreams of Malay youth, particularly those in isolated rural areas. A lot of the speeches were funny, given in a mixture of Malay and English. None of them were boring.

So there I was, Jessica McKinnock, listening with interest to speech after speech, and the next minute I'm gazing into the most beautiful darkest of dark-brown eyes I have ever seen. And I'm drowning in them.

Suddenly the whole world changed. Became a different place. Like I had been bumped up onto another plane. No, it was like my eyes were sealed shut and suddenly they popped open. I'm not describing this right. I could cry, this is so hard to explain. It was like I recognized him. I knew him and hadn't seen him for ages and wasn't expecting him, but there he was. And I was *so* happy to see him. Love at first sight? But it didn't feel like "at first sight." It felt like "meeting again after all this time." Like our souls knew each other...and they say your soul is in your eyes.

It was towards the end of the speeches. A young woman was introducing the president of their federation, talking about his leadership and calling him a visionary. Two things I remember clearly: (1) I was thinking to myself that this youth leader sounded pretty amazing and I couldn't wait to hear what he had to say and (2) I was suddenly aware that one of the guys on the dais was staring at me.

Now, as far as I can tell it's not rude to stare at people here. Anyway, everyone's always staring at us and by now we're used to it. The way I deal with it is—I stare back. And that's when it happened. This weird feeling of *déjà vu*. The person I was staring at was totally familiar to me even though I had never seen him before. He was dressed all in white, except for the black sash around his waist and the black fez set firmly on his forehead. The blinding white showed off the rich brown colour of his skin. His features were squarish but lean, darkly handsome, and though he was sitting in a relaxed way there was something intense and quietly powerful about him, like a panther resting. But it was his eyes that got me. They glittered like a winter's midnight. I knew immediately that he was sharp and intelligent, incredibly alive and *there*. Those eyes were the total opposite of dull. And they stared at me as if they knew me.

I could hardly believe myself, but I beamed a big smile at him, as if it were the most natural thing to do, the only thing to do. He stood up, and I nearly panicked as I thought he was going to step off the dais and come over to talk to me, right in the middle of the speeches! But of course, he went over to the microphone. His name had been called out.

Haji Ahmed Muhammed Bin Muhammed Rahman. President of the National Federation of Islamic Youth in Malaysia.

I sure can pick them.

(Writing again later, after kitchen duty):

But then, he picked me out too, didn't he? All through his speech he kept looking over at me. It wasn't my imagination. At one point Katie whispered to me, "What a cutie-pie," and I nodded, but then about five minutes later she whispered again, "Hey, I think he's got his eye on you. Yum, yum." My throat felt dry, I could hardly swallow. That confirmed it wasn't wishful thinking on my part.

His speech was wonderful. Very personal, which again was so different from the usual official stuff. He didn't use notes, but talked away in a flow of English and Malay and

116

occasionally Arabic when he quoted from the Qur'an. He spoke about growing up on a rural *kampung* in Terengganu and how it taught him the values of Islam in everyday life with his family and his neighbours. Then he went on the pilgrimage to Mecca. The whole world opened up to him as there were Muslims there from every corner of the globe, and he saw hardship and suffering as well as happiness and freedom. Then his first year at university in K.L. opened his eyes to all the possibilities for himself and more so, his country. When he met young Malaysians of Indian and Chinese and other ethnic origins, he realized the need for each group to know clearly who they were, where they came from and what they wanted in their future. Each group needed to be secure and strong in themselves, so they could meet each other with confidence. Tolerance of others is only possible if one is sure of oneself, at peace with one's place in society and in the world.

I listened avidly to his speech, because he was talking about everything that our project stood for and he was expressing it in such a powerful and beautiful way. It's hard to describe his voice as it changed, depending on the language he was speaking. He sounded like he was singing when he spoke Arabic, or chanting more like. Of course I stared at him the whole time. That's the great thing about being in the audience and watching someone on stage. You can stare away to your heart's content. But every time he looked my way and our eyes met and he smiled around his words, I felt my heart leap, like it was trapped inside and yearning to get out. (Oh gawd, this sounds so stupid, like a Harlequin romance, but it's not. It's so incredibly, amazingly wonderful.)

After the speeches there was the usual buffet set out for everyone, long tables laden with teapots and Malaysian goodies. It's funny how we ignore the egg-salad sandwiches these days and go straight for the *gula melaka*, prawn *mee*, *laksa* and *keropok*. I was reaching across to pop some rice cake onto my plate (dieting we are not) when I suddenly sensed him beside me. Now this is the weirdest part of all. Normally if I feel this way about someone—stop right there, I've never felt this way about anyone—well, normally if I'm attracted to a guy and build up any kind of fantasy about him, if he even comes near me I'm a goner. I get all flustered, tongue-tied, red in the face and die die die. But it wasn't that way at all with Ahmed. As soon as he spoke, it felt so natural, so easy, so right.

"Hello, my sister."

I just smiled at him at first. It was so nice having him there beside me, staring straight into his eyes. It was as if there was no one else in the hall, no one else on the entire planet, except us two, meeting together at last. I said his name.

"Ahmed."

He nodded, smiled back, offered the plate of egg-salad sandwiches which I declined. He was waiting.

"*Nama saya* Jessica. *Apa khabar?*"

His eyebrows went up, like two birds leaving the branch, and I could see he was delighted. He hadn't expected to hear his language on my tongue.

"*Baik-lah*, Jessie-cah!"

He laughed, a rolling sort of a laugh that washed over me. It felt so good. I had made him happy. Our first conversation was in Malay. He asked me questions, about my

118

home, my school, my friends, my church. At first I stumbled through the answers, but eventually I grew more confident in his sheer appreciation of my efforts. It was as if he were Malaysia itself inclining a gentle ear towards me, savouring every word and nodding with encouragement. He kept repeating softly, "*Baik-lah*, Jessie-cah. *Baik-lah*."


February 10, 1973

*U*p early for our first day at work. Two Land Rovers arrived to pick us up and bring us into the countryside to plant rice in the paddy fields. I had butterflies in my stomach all morning and got up earlier than usual to try on different outfits. I knew he would be there. He told me his youth group was working with us in the afternoon. Katie woke up when I was trying on my third sarong and T-shirt. (I wanted the best colours to show off my hair, which I decided, like a madwoman, to leave loose. Chose blue in the end.) Katie looked bleary-eyed at the clock—5:30 a.m.—groaned, then looked back at me and at the clothes scattered all over my bed. She started to sing the theme of *Love Story* in a croaky voice. What a card.

Well, my hair didn't stay loose for long. Once we started working it was totally in the way and I had to tie it back with a kerchief one of the women gave me. The paddy fields were flat, flooded with water and partitioned by raised banks of mud and grass. When we stepped in, barefooted, we sank into the mud up to our knees. Not easy to keep your balance, let me tell you, and it's an awful sensation when the muck oozes between your toes. Our sarongs

119

were caught up between our legs and tucked in at the waist, and we were given conical straw hats to keep off the sun.

Our job was to plant the young shoots of rice. We used a two-pronged fork to shove them into the mud, leaving the green tops above the water to get air. It's back-breaking work since you're bending over all the time and only the women do it, as they say rice planted by men won't grow. The men are the ones who plough the fields with water buffalo and, during the planting season, they walk up and down the banks handing out the clumps of shoots. Some of the women were very old, skinny and wiry, and they worked so quickly they made it look easy. But it wasn't. After a half-hour I was exhausted and my back was aching. To think they do this hour after hour, day after day! So much for the weaker sex.

At one point I stopped to look around me. It was like a Chinese painting: figures in pointed hats bent over the rice fields, palm trees wavering against a cloudless sky. Then I heard a yelp behind me and a big splash and I turned around to see Cyn disappear under the water. She re-emerged a second later looking like the monster from the deep lagoon, her hair plastered against her face and every part of her dripping. We couldn't help ourselves, we had to laugh as two old women hauled her out of the paddy. Chuckling to themselves, they took Cyn away to a *kampung* house to clean her up.

Things were quieting down when Louise let out a blood-curdling scream. She lifted her leg out of the water. It was covered in leeches! Total gross-out. We were all screeching then as we discovered them on our legs. A few of the Malay men jumped into the water and shaved the leeches off us with their *parangs*. Louise jumped out and refused to do any more, but Katie got a great idea. She kept lighting up cigarettes to burn them off. One touch and they drop like flies. So much for not smoking in public, but we all kept a cigarette in our mouths after that. (Yuk, but the leeches were yukker.) Louise took over the job of handing out the shoots and our guys decided they wanted to plant. The Malays thought this was funny, there was lots of laughing and calling them women, but they let them do it. Hope the rice grows!

At lunch-time we stopped working and went to a *kampung* house nearby. There was a huge picnic laid out on the grass, under the palm trees. The rattan mats were covered with dishes of cold rice, prawns, fish in chili peppers, curries, bananas, rambutans and *kelapa muda* (young coconut). We ate with our hands (right only), the girls sitting with the women and the guys with the men. The conversations were in English and Malay and everyone was saying how surprised they were that we were working with them. They had never seen *orang puteh* working in a rice paddy in their lives.

I was having so much fun that I actually forgot about Ahmed coming and I didn't hear the bus drive up with the youth workers. Lunch was over and I was helping to wash the dishes at the well. The other women started to giggle when he came over (guess he's a dreamboat by their standards as well as mine) and he greeted them all in Malay with that wonderful smile of his. I must have looked a sight in my bare feet, with splashes of mud on my sarong and my hair all over the place. He looked so clean and neat, in a blue shirt and the checkered sarong the *kampung* men wear.

121

(It's amazing how fantastic a man can look in a skirt!) His smile was even bigger when he looked at me.

"You have been working hard, my sister."

I laughed and kept pushing my hair out of my face. I felt shy but not awkward.

We walked together along the banks of the paddy we were to work that afternoon. The others were already wading into the water. Ahmed laughed when he saw our guys planting with the women. Then he told me a story about how the agricultural development authority had tried to introduce double-cropping into poorer areas. The new system was explained to the men, with meetings, slides and the whole bit. The farmers seemed to accept that it would bring them prosperity and yet nothing happened. The system never got going. After investigating the matter, they realized that no one had consulted the women, the ones who planted the rice, and so *they* were brought in, more meetings, more slides, and guess what. Double-cropping arrived.

"You can't introduce change unless everyone understands it," Ahmed said with a grin.

"Who says women have no power," I agreed.

Then I asked him for his opinion on women. Maybe I shouldn't have, it's against the project rules (wading into deep water, wondering about the leeches) but I wanted to know what he thought. He didn't mind and I guess I knew he wouldn't. Everything he said in his speech the other day, and just the way he was, told me he was open to discussion.

"I honour my mother," he said, "and all women who are my sisters, those in my family, those I work with, those I meet in the course of my life. I will honour my wife one day. How could I do otherwise? It is written so in the Qur'an, which is the word of God. But do you want me to speak of the difference between Muslim women and Western women? I know very little about Western women, though I have heard about them and of course there is television. But as I'm sure you have discovered also—from living and working with Muslims—what you hear from others and what you experience for yourself is not the same thing. You are the first Western woman I have known in person. Without meaning to offend, Jessie-cah, you do not seem strange to me. You do not look or act as I imagined a Western woman would. But perhaps you are a different person in your own country?"

He frowned and gave me a searching look. I didn't know what to say at first. He had me there, caught in his gaze, wriggling a bit. But after a moment, I knew the truth of it.

"I act differently here," I explained, "to fit in better, to belong. I might say or do things I wouldn't do at home. But really the difference isn't that great and nowhere near as big as I had thought it would be. I'm still the same person, I believe in the same things and I feel the same way. In Canada or Malaysia, this is me."

His frown disappeared. He smiled again, so warmly that it felt like the sun shining down on me. *Baik-lah, Jessie-cah.*


February 12, 1973

*T*oday was the last day for planting rice and we finished after lunch. Everyone exchanged addresses to be pen-pals. (I'll have to write to hundreds of people when I get back!) It was such a wonderful experience, and working with Ahmed every day was the icing on the cake. He didn't plant rice, but stayed on the banks distributing the shoots. He was the one who always gave them to me. The other men made comments to him in Malay and Ahmed would laugh back and wave the rice at them as if pretending to fight. At lunch he sat with the men but would look over at me from time to time. That made the women nudge each other and laugh behind their hands. I didn't mind. I figured it would have been the same if I was a Malay girl—except our parents would probably be arranging our marriage! (Sigh.) Funny how people can always tell when a boy and girl like each other. I mean, all we were doing was looking. But it was so delicious. Like a long drink of coconut milk to a dry throat after work.

At break times we would sit under the palm trees, all the workers, and drink from the *kelapa muda*. One of the smaller boys would run up a tree—the trunks are marked with notches like steps—to knock down the nuts with his *parang*. They're nothing like the dried coconuts you get at Hallowe'en. Fresh from the tree, they're a big green thing the size of a football, with the brown kernel inside full of milky water. The Malays chop off the top so you can drink the juice as if from a cup. When it's empty, they hack the nut in half and you scoop out the soft fleshy pulp with a spoon. Yum.

Everyone would sit around together, talking about how much we had done or how much more we needed to do and who was getting married and who had babies and whose kids were at school and stuff. It felt so natural, sitting in the shade of the trees, the rice fields stretching out beyond us, and always, always, Ahmed smiling over at me. Sometimes he and I would walk together along the banks (more giggling from the women and toothy grins from the men) and we would talk and talk: about the project and our lives, Canada and Malaysia, school and future plans. Nothing profound really, but every moment was heaven to me, as if the day had never shone so brightly and the world had never been so perfect. I could have walked along those banks, under those palm trees, with him...forever.

When I think about it, sitting here writing this (with a moony look on my face, says Katie, who came in to get her purse), in Canada I would have thought it odd that we didn't hold hands or kiss or anything. But there's no question of us doing that. Muslim boys and girls don't mix together, don't touch each other, until they're married. That's not the odd thing about it though, but rather the fact that I didn't feel the need to. It felt right exactly the way it was.

Today being our last day, I was very sad, especially at the thought of saying goodbye to Ahmed. I guess he sensed it, because he asked my why I was quiet and was I unhappy? I shrugged and said I was wondering if I would ever see him again. He laughed and said of course I would, as his group would be working with us again and then he invited me to the *kampung* where he lives to meet his parents! He's going to borrow his uncle's car and pick me up Friday. Hurrah!!! I'm over the moon. I'm walking on air.

Can't write any more. Lise is shouting up the stairs that the mini-bus is here. We're going to visit a batik factory. I'm off.

## February 13, 1973

*I* was too tired last night to write about the factory, as we were invited to free outdoor movies with some of the kids who live around here. Like in Malacca, our neighbours wander in and out of the house and invite us to their homes for meals and visits. All the girls have nicknames: Zubaidah is Dah, Masnah is Mah, Faziah is Zah, Norazimi is Zimi. All the guys are either Kamil or Muhammed. Our guys hang around with the guys, the girls with the girls.

At the movies, everyone sat on the ground around a big screen. There were two movies, all in Malay, no subtitles, one in colour and one in black and white. The first one was about the international Qur'an reading competition which every Islamic country takes part in. Malaysia usually wins—right on! The second was about the pilgrimage to Mecca which is every Muslim's dream, the peak of their life if they can manage it. Going by air is very expensive, so many take the long journey by boat around India. If a man goes, he has "Haji" put in front of his name. If a woman goes, she becomes "Hajia." There were snacks afterwards, long chewy sticks of prawn dropped into a cauldron of boiling oil, and sticks of sugar cane to suck and chew.

## February 14, 1973

*V* alentine's Day and for the first time in my life I can really and truly say I am in love. It's not celebrated here so I won't get chocolates from Ahmed! Only one more day till I see him. *A loaf of bread, a jug of wine and thou...*

Our new project, planting *kachang* (ground nuts), only lasted till noon. It was so hot and humid, we couldn't keep going. A lot of the kids, especially the guys, slacked off. We're so lazy, spoiled Westerners I guess. I see the Malay women cleaning the street gutters and even doing construction on the roads with shovels and picks, and it makes me wonder—why are some people's lives so much harder than others'?

More socializing today. Rosnah invited me, Louise, Katie and Cyn to her house to learn Malay cooking. (Lise was meeting officials about our schedule. So glad I'm not a group leader.) Rosnah's house is quite big, made of wood, with a shady area underneath where the showers and kitchen are. The townhouses don't have stilts, but there are stone floors on the ground level which make it cool.

We got out the frying pans and loads of tiny fish (*ikan kembong*) which we had bought at the market. Katie cut and gutted them and when the Malay girls praised her work, she rolled her eyes and said, "I knows my fish, b'y." We did everything imaginable to those little fish: stuffed them with chilis, fried them with spices, baked them in sauces and stewed them in curries. I wrote down my favourite recipe to cook it for the group on my next turn in the kitchen. Can't imagine being able to do it in Canada, but I'll try:

*Makanan Melayu* (Malay Food)

Utensils:  *batu geling* (crusher with a stone roller)
 *badang* (to cook the rice)

Spices (*rampah*):  *kunyit* (tumeric)
  *bawang puteh* (white onion)
  *bawang merah* (green onion)
  *halia* (ginger)
  *adamanis* (sweetener)
  *lada hitam* (black pepper)
  *aji-no-moto* (Japanese
  flavouring)

(Meals are prepared while squatting on the floor.)

To cook *ikan kembong* (fish):
1. scrape pulp of fish and remove bones, cut into chunks
2. cut up green onions, onions and chilis, into small pieces
3. mash together with other spices in *batu geling*
4. fry all together in oil

Then we tried prawn chips. What a hoot. You throw the prawn—heads, tails and shells removed—into very hot oil and, ta dah, it explodes into a chip!

We ate everything we made, with plain rice and cups of sugary tea. I pigged out totally. There was a big crowd of us, all the girls who hang around together, Mah, Dah, etc. and some of their younger sisters. The kitchen was full and we spilled out into the yard. Everyone was firing questions at us. Would we go to university? What age would we marry at? Would our parents pick our husbands? Would we have careers? Would we have children? Could we have both? Did we have servants? Were we all rich? Did we really want to choose our own husbands? What if we made a mistake? Didn't we think our parents knew better since they were older and already married?

I have to say we were on our toes, but for once we weren't worried about giving "the right answers" or presenting "the right image." There were no media or official representatives about, just girls talking together about their lives. We answered as honestly as we could. Katie got a good laugh for her answer to "Would you marry a Malay boy?"—"Which one?"

We asked questions about their lives too and, of course, what we were most curious about—arranged marriages. They were all too young to be married, but most of their older sisters were. Rosnah said she was going to give her parents a list of what she wanted in a husband. But in fact the arrangements are made with the girl's and guy's consent, with people they know, people they expect to marry. I guess in a small community it must become obvious in time who's right for who and everyone sort of knows who they'll marry anyway. When the parents get involved, they help the couple set up.

The afternoon was great fun. For all the cultural or social differences, they weren't that different from us. They were all bright, confident, talkative, curious, full of life, with opinions, dreams and ideas. Some will go to university because their families can afford to send them. Others just want to get married and have families. But it's the same at home. Shirley says all she wants is "a Mrs. degree and a colour TV." Some of the girls are youth leaders of both male and female groups. I couldn't help thinking of the Western idea of Muslim women. I mean, if they were living in some terrible anti-woman society, wouldn't it show? How come they don't act like they're downtrodden or oppressed or whatever?

Dah won a big competition for Qur'an recital and she does beautiful calligraphy as well, in the *jawi* script (Arabic writing). You could tell the others thought she was special and that she would be someone important one day. (There are Malay women in politics). She is very pretty and petite, with long dark hair that she wears under a kerchief all the time, as the stricter Muslim girls do. She's quieter than the others, very intelligent. I just realized something and it hurts inside. She would make a perfect wife for Ahmed.

They asked us about our guys and were any of them our boyfriends.

"Claude belongs to Louise but you can have your pick of the rest of them," was my answer, which made them laugh.

"Do you like Malay boy?"

That must be the million-dollar question here, every Malay girl asks us. Cyn nodded enthusiastically (Yusuf phones her at least once a week and is planning a visit). I got flustered, which triggered off a fit of giggles and some fast whispering in Malay in which I caught Ahmed's name. News travels fast in a small place. I detected looks of envy sent my way. Am I right in thinking he's the eligible bachelor of the year?

After *makanan* we went to Mah's house to *joget* (dance). Her mother welcomed us into their home, everyone bowing their heads and shaking hands and touching their hearts. They had an old record player and put on Malay music. We had taken our shoes off before coming in, of course, so we danced barefoot. The floor was thumping under Louise and me and, I'm not sure, but I think the walls were shaking too. We both got so embarrassed we sat down and insisted we would rather watch. (That's it. Louise and I have sworn to start dieting tomorrow.) Cyn and Katie are both still slender, though they eat as much as we do, and they looked very graceful dancing with the others. Katie's tiny size blends in with the Malay girls and she would look like them if it weren't for the flaming red hair and freckles. Cyn is a good head or two taller and moves like a swan. I was feeling kind of sad and left out, Lousie too, but then they decided to teach us the candle dance. There was no hopping about in this one, so we got up again.

It was fantastic. They stuck small candles in saucers (lighted!) which you balance in the palms of your hands. Then with arm and wrist movements you turn the saucers under and over your arms, over your head, around your body, all the time gliding slowly, kneeling down and standing up again. We had to be careful not to set our *baju kurongs* alight. Katie got too close at one point and singed my hair! At last Mah said we were ready to perform.

She called in her parents, brothers and a few of the neighbours. The lights went out, the music rose up, and there we were: in a house in Terengganu, on a warm Malaysian evening, Arabic music ringing out so sweet and mournful, all of us in long flowing dresses and bare feet, dancing with fire.

It was Valentine's Day. I danced with an image in my head and heart, the face of my beloved hidden in the shadows, to whom I offered the light in the palm of my hands.

February 15, 1973

*I* should write what happened last night when we got home from Mah's. Katie and I found gigantic bugs in our beds! There was a dead scorpion in hers and a giant beetle on mine, decapitated. We screeched, we were so grossed out. Mine was right on my pillow. We knew Ray and Darren were the culprits, as we had put frogs in their shoes the day before. Revenge was necessary and we sneaked over to their room with jugs of cold water. But they had locked the door. We could hear them sniggering on the other side. Then I got a great idea. We threw sugar through the screens on top of the doors, tons of it that must have landed everywhere. It was only a matter of time before the ants came trooping in. Katie started singing, "*Di gigit semut, siapa sakit naik atas,*" a Malay kid's song about ants. I joined in. The guys were yelling and cursing. Next minute lights went on all over the place and everyone was yelling at us, girls and guys. Lise came storming out of her room, cursing in French, to order everyone back to bed like a *serjan mejar.* We're in deep shit today. Nobody's talking to Katie or me. But hey, was it worth it? You bet.

Went shopping after work today. (It's a killer job, bending down and placing one nut at a time in a long straight row. I wouldn't mind if Ahmed were there but we're working with a boy scout troop this week.) I cashed a traveller's cheque and got 25 Malay *ringgits* for $10 Canadian. I should have changed my money when we first arrived like Katie did. The dollar was worth more than three times its value last month. Katie only brought $100 for her entire stay—her life's savings—and her family doesn't send money in their letters like mine does. I tried to give her some of mine but she got mad and said she didn't take charity. I wouldn't be too proud to take money off someone who's got more than me (i.e., Mom and Dad) but maybe that's different? If you're poor all the time, does money mean more than just money, something personal as well? I wanted to ask Katie but she's very touchy on certain subjects. When she gets her Irish up, she can explode and I don't want that directed at me, thank you very much.

I bought some more talcum powder. Mah and Rosnah told us to rub it on our faces to keep from sweating all the time. They wander around with skin dusted white with powder. It looked funny at first but now I'm used to it. I also bought a little tin of tiger balm which they said is the best remedy for headaches. You rub it on your forehead and it feels soothing. Smells like eucalyptus. We had *roti canai* for lunch in a *restoran*, floury pancakes that you dip into a curried corn sauce. Katie thinks there's something addictive in them because we have them at least once a day and often three or four times! So much for dieting.

## February 19, 1973

*I*'m back from my weekend at Ahmed's home, Atas Tol, a rural *kampung* outside of Kuala Terengganu. Katie and Cyn are dying to hear all about it (the others too, nosy parkers) but I want to write everything down while it's fresh in my mind. I didn't take my journal with me, as it would have been "bad manners" (Gran) to be writing about my hosts while I was living with them. Anyway, there was no sitting up late at night with the lights on to write. I slept on a mat in a room with Ahmed's younger sisters, Aysha and Norihma.

Ahmed came to pick me up in his uncle's car, an old Ford as big as a chariot. I was surprised to see a woman in the back seat and then realized, of course, that the two of us couldn't travel alone through the countryside. Ahmed introduced me to his older sister, Fatimah. She had a little fat-cheeked baby wrapped in a shawl and fast asleep on her lap. Fatimah was shy at first. Though a few years older than her brother, she didn't have his confidence and seemed to wait for his opinions and directions. I liked the way he talked to her. His tone was always respectful and considerate and he kept asking if she and the baby were comfortable. When we passed a roadside stall, he stopped to get fruit drinks and rice packets for all of us, handing them first to Fatimah.

It was a long trip, but the baby never cried. I couldn't believe it. He did let out a yowl when he woke up, but that stopped as soon as it started. In the front seat, I turned around at his cry and got embarrassed when I realized that he was being breast-fed. Not that you could see anything with the shawl around him, but I could hear his happy gurgling sounds. Fatimah saw me blush and she apologized for not giving him a bottle. Something odd happened then, because Ahmed spoke suddenly in Malay, very firmly to Fatimah, and before I knew it they were arguing. They didn't raise their voices but it was obviously a disagreement as both were shaking their heads. The words came so quickly, and in the Terengganu dialect, I couldn't understand them. But with their own language, a subtle change occurred.

They were more equal now and I could see Fatimah asserting herself as a quiet, older sister. She was simply less confident in English and in the presence of a "European" stranger.

Ahmed was quite angry. The way he held himself stiffly as he drove and the hard set of his mouth surprised me. When he finally explained in English what they were talking about, I discovered it wasn't Fatimah he was angry at.

"The foreign companies who sell formula for babies send their salespeople to our *kampungs* dressed in white coats like nurses and doctors. They tell the women that bottle-feeding is the modern way and better for their children. Fatimah's English isn't good and she was confused by the instructions. She decided to feed her baby the way our mother fed us. The traditional way. The natural way. Fatimah's baby is much healthier than her friends' babies who are bottle-fed. He is fatter, stronger, and he rarely cries or falls ill. I am hoping the other women will see this and understand the lie they've been told."

It was the longest speech he ever made to me. I'm touched by the fact that it was about women and children.

My heart lifted at the first sight of Atas Tol. It is a quiet green place with *kampung* houses dotted here and there among the palm trees. Extremely neat and tidy, it has an air of modest prosperity and a strong neighbourhood feeling that reminded me of Calabogie. There was no Western clothing in sight. The women wore loose-flowing *baju kurongs* and light kerchiefs on their heads, all of bright colours. They walked with parasols to shade them from the sun. The men wore sarongs with cotton shirts and sandals. Ahmed changed into his as soon as he arrived home.

His house was lovely, all of dark wood, with a high peaked ceiling and arched windows with blue shutters. When we entered (shoes left on the step), his whole family was there to welcome me. His two little sisters, bright as buttons, were so excited they climbed all over me. His mother, *Puan* (Mrs.) Rahman, cupped my hands and touched her heart. She looked so young and serenely beautiful. That's where Ahmed gets his looks from. *Encik* (Mr.) Rahman is more chunky, plainer-faced, and older than his wife, the kind of man who chuckles a lot. He made me feel immediately at ease.

There was an incredible supper waiting for us, made especially for my visit, I think; *nasi lemak*, rice cooked in coconut milk with peanuts and cucumber, served alongside *rendang*, a spicy meat dish. For dessert, I had my first taste of durian. *Encik* Rahman warned me that I would either love it or hate it and that I wasn't to feel obliged to eat it. Everyone had their eyes glued on me as a big slice of the yellow fruit was set on my plate. For a moment I thought it was a test, and then I realized that Ahmed was trying not to laugh even as Fatimah protested that they shouldn't be teasing me. Something told me this was *Encik* Rahman's idea as he's obviously a real joker. The truth is durian has the most awful stink—like the oldest smelliest socks imaginable!—and yet it tastes like a dream. I can't describe it. It is simply itself and not like anything else. But now I know why it's the most popular fruit in Malaysia.

I ate the whole thing to the applause and hilarity of my audience. It was a perfect moment, because I felt like part of the family, all those laughing faces around me as they shared my first reaction to the *fruit terrible*.

After dinner, Fatimah's husband came to collect her as she lives outside the *kampung*. The rest of us relaxed with cups of *kopi-o* (*café au lait*). *Encik* Rahman asked me questions about my parents and my home and if we were a religious family. I explained that we went to church once a week and that my mom used to read the Bible to us when we were kids, especially on winter nights. He beamed with approval at that and was interested in the fact that Dad was an active Elder before his heart stopped him from doing his duties.

"We are a good Muslim home," *Encik* Rahman said. "We recite Qur'an together and we pray five times a day. We pay *zaka'at* to help the poor and we fast in the month of Ramadan. We have sent our son to Mecca and, *Insha Allah* (God willing), the rest of us will go too before we die. These are the five pillars of Islam along with our faith that there is one God and Muhammed (peace be upon him) is his prophet."

When it was time for the evening prayer, they invited me to join them as anyone who has "a believing heart" is welcome to pray with Muslims. I hesitated at first as I wasn't sure of myself or what it might mean for me as a Christian, whether it would be wrong or not. Then in a flash it struck me. *There is one God.* Though we have different religions, it's the same Being we all pray to. And since I haven't been able to attend a service here, this was my chance to worship in community.

*Puan* Rahman showed me how to wash for prayers; hands, mouth, nostrils, face, right arm, then left, top of the head, ears, neck and finally feet. She and the girls were done in seconds, but the first few times it took me much longer as it was all so new to me. (I nearly died when she asked me if I was having my period as that would have exempted me from prayers the whole weekend. She also offered me a kerchief for my hair, but I had brought the one Dah gave me and put it on.)

I can see how they are able to pray five times a day without too much trouble. By the second day, I sensed when prayer time had arrived, though it was hard at first getting up so early in the morning for the one before sunrise. But it only took a few minutes. They pray quietly and very fast, all in Arabic, and the movements are second nature to Believers since they do it so often. *Encik* Rahman would lead the prayers in front, on his own mat, with Ahmed next, and the women and girls behind, sharing a carpet. We always faced northwest, in the direction of Mecca. I would copy their movements, standing, bowing, sitting, touching my head to the mat (which smelled of perfume). Each time we prayed was an amazing experience. Though I could only listen to the words, I felt them lift me up and carry me along, like a leaf floating downstream in a current of light. It was exactly the same feeling I get in church whenever we sing my favourite hymn, Psalm 23.

Of course the entire time I was there I was never alone with Ahmed and never expected to be. The two girls followed us everywhere (their big brother is their idol, especially since Fatimah got married). We did a lot of visiting in the *kampung*. The entire extended family wanted to meet me—grandparents, aunts, uncles, cousins, relations-in-law of Fatimah's and so on. That meant a lot of eating and also chatting, mostly in Malay as few people spoke English there. Ahmed translated whenever I got stuck.

But it didn't matter that we were never alone. I was in a

state of bliss, wandering about as if in a dream. It was just so wonderful that we were together, there in his home, in the heart of Malaysia. This kind of feeling for another human being, this kind of love, how can it be anything other than a gift?

There are two images I have of my visit which glow in my mind like candles, never to be extinguished.

We were sitting on chairs on the veranda in the warm evening breeze, watching the last fiery rays of the sunset, just after prayers. Ahmed was telling me stories about the Prophet as I had said I wanted to know more about him. Aysha and Norihma were struggling for the best position on my lap (they are four and six respectively) and finally Ahmed took Aysha to settle the matter. He told me about Muhammed's escape from Mecca, when his enemies were trying to kill him. The Prophet hid in a cave with his best friend and companion, Abu Bakr. They could hear the assassins combing the mountains around them and Abu Bakr grew afraid.

"We are but two," said Abu Bakr anxiously.

"Nay," said Muhammed, "for Allah is with us."

And he pointed to the mouth of the cave. Spiders had woven huge webs across it so that when the soldiers came, they figured no one had entered there and they didn't search it. Unharmed, Muhammed and Abu Bakr continued their flight to Medina. That year, the year of the flight or *hijrah*, is the first year of the Islamic calendar.

"You tell a story now," Norihma demanded.

Since I knew from Yusuf that Muslims respect Jesus— *'Isa* they call him—I told them the story of the tempest at sea. How Jesus had gone fishing with his disciples but fell

139

asleep just before a gale blew up. The other fishermen grew so afraid that they woke him.

"Lord save us," they cried, "we perish."

"Why are ye fearful?" Jesus said. "Oh ye of little faith."

But though he was saddened that they didn't know they were safe with him, he calmed the waters and the winds.

Aysha and Norihma clapped when I was finished and demanded more, so we continued with tales of Muhammed and Jesus till their bedtime.

My other memory is a painful one but beautiful all the same. I was with *Puan* Rahman in the kitchen section at the back of the house, helping her prepare supper. There was a curtained doorway to the room, a low ceiling, straw mats on the floor, a gas stove in the corner and a big jar that held water from the well. Malay women prepare food squatting on the floor, and the cooking utensils were spread out on rattan mats. My job was to scrape the soft white pulp of the coconut and squeeze it through a sifter to make *santan*, the creamy base of the curry. *Puan* Rahman and I spoke mostly in Malay. She wanted to know all about my family, but mostly about the women, Mom and what her life was like, and then Gran when I mentioned her. She was surprised that Gran was living with us, as she had heard that we don't look after our old people in the West.

It was cool and shady where we worked and the back door was open onto the blazing sunlight outside. At one point, Ahmed came into sight, carrying sticks to light a bonfire for the rubbish. (He had chores to do all weekend. There's no question of him being a spoiled college boy who gets to take it easy or just study at home.) I guess I stared out the doorway at him a bit longer than I should have, because when I turned back to what I was doing, I realized that *Puan* Rahman was watching me. I met her look for a moment, then lowered my eyes. It was obvious that she saw, that she knew. I didn't try to hide it. But her look was one of such quiet sympathy that I almost broke down.

I'm not going to write any more. I feel so sad. I miss Ahmed and his family. I just want to lie on my bed and stare out at the blue sky and think about them.

### February 20, 1973

*T*his afternoon we had a meeting to do Operation 12, an assessment of our projects in Malacca and Terengganu; what we liked best, what we liked least, what we learned, ideas for improvement and so on. There were forms to fill out and then we talked as a group about what we felt we got from the experience. Val was there with a tape recorder. He's on a circuit, doing this with all the groups. We were asked to discuss the programme for 1974, suggestions on structure, training, schedules, projects, etc.

First and foremost everyone stressed language. We all agreed it must be the top priority, French and English for the Canadians, and as much of the host country language as possible. It's so obviously the first and greatest bridge to cross and by the same token, the greatest barrier.

We didn't have our usual all-out bitching session and not a single argument! I think it was the tape, but also the fact that we were laying groundwork for the next bunch of kids to undergo this experience. Sometimes it's easy to forget that this is the first year of the project, the pilot programme.

It's a whole new world and we're the pioneers, pulling up stumps and clearing the way so others can come here too.

It was interesting looking around at the group. We looked so different from our training days in Canada! All the girls were in Malay dress, the boys in sarongs, everyone brown and healthy-looking though the girls have got plump and the boys skinny! Nobody looked out of place or uncomfortable. It was like we all belonged right where we were, right then and there. I suddenly saw what a big jump we had made.

Lise in fact made a little speech after the assessment which confirmed it all. She said we should be proud of ourselves, that we had come through culture shock with flying colours and made the adjustment to the new country, climate, culture and most importantly, people. It was after Val left that she said this (he's on a tight schedule, moving from group to group) and then she told us the Big Stuff. She said we would probably hear it in letters from other participants anyway. Apparently some of the other groups are not doing so well at all, in fact two have broken up completely!!! Their group leaders went home and a load of the kids did too. The ones who decided to stay have been divided among the other groups, but Val decided not to send anyone to us because we were doing the best and he didn't want to disturb our balance.

Like, knock me down with a feather. Everyone's eyes bugged out.

"I'm gob-smacked," declared Katie.

It's the story of the ugly duckling! I mean, we were the worst group in the training camps and even Val had his doubts that we could pull through Malaysia together because we fought so much. He was afraid we might "fragment like a bad marriage under stress." But then again, he had hoped we would "harness the negative energy and put it to the good." That was his best-case scenario, if I remember rightly, and it's turned out to be true!

I asked Lise point-blank what went wrong in the groups that broke up. She hesitated at first, didn't want to go into it, and you could see she was debating how much she should tell us.

"We're not children," I said firmly. "We have a right to know what's going on."

I was amazed at my own directness. Katie threw me an admiring glance and backed me up. (Hey—will I be able to talk this way with Mom and Dad when I get home? There's so much stuff in my family that nobody talks about and none of us kids ever had the courage to ask. Like what happened that time Mom disappeared for a few weeks and Auntie Gillian arrived in a big hush and flurry? And what about Uncle Bill? Why is he the black sheep and not allowed to visit?)

Anyway, Lise finally agreed that things shouldn't be kept secret, though she admitted she was afraid we might start thinking along the same lines that led to the groups breaking up. She said because our group was doing so well she was afraid to interfere or tamper with the process, but of course as a leader she should trust us to know what's best for ourselves. She quoted Mahatma Gandhi: "There go my people, I must follow them as I am their leader." (Far out.)

So why did the two groups break up? No one's certain if it was the leaders or the participants who first started the idea, but somehow all the letters—from the leaders who resigned and the participants who dropped out—said the same thing; namely, that they felt they were intruding on the Malaysian people and disrupting Malaysian life with their Western presence and influences. We were a burden on the Malaysians, they said, those who had to look after us and feed us and entertain us. We were interrupting their lives with our selfish needs. The bottom line was we shouldn't be here. It's unethical. Wrong. One more imposition of the West on other nations and their peoples.

It did knock me back. Actually, all of us looked a bit shaken because none of us had even thought of it that way or considered the project from that angle. I guess we were having so much fun and the Malaysians we meet seem to love having us here. But are we imposing on them? The government people have to make arrangements for us and tours and official stuff. The villagers and townspeople could ignore us if they wanted to, couldn't they? I mean, they invite us into their homes because they have their own natural curiosity about us. They definitely get a great kick out of us. I mean, we're entertaining them as much as they entertain us!

We had a discussion on the question of our intrusion. Ray pointed out that the Malaysians watch Western television programmes so their culture has already been invaded by the West. Claude agreed and pointed out that, in a small way, as people meeting people, we might lessen some of the worse evils of Western influence and show that it's not just a big commercial thing. Plus, by us being here, the West is being influenced by the East for a change. I mean, none of us will be the same after this and that will include people we know in Canada as we share our experiences with them.

This project is all about Malaysia influencing *us*. Katie said the whole world is in this together for better or worse and it's impossible for any country or group to stay separate any more, even if they wanted to. And the Malaysians don't seem to want to stay separate. They obviously intend to be a strong voice in the world family.

But still, you could tell everyone was disturbed. I mentioned the bottle-feeding thing that Ahmed had spoken about. The evils of Western influence. It's something we'll all be thinking about now. Should we be here? Are we doing any harm to the Malaysians? If they like us, might they think they can trust the West and then get ripped off? Are we a propaganda front, like the Peace Corps, to cover Western business influences and who knows what else? I'm feeling paranoid about this. I don't trust governments, not even my own. I'm going to ask Ahmed about it. We're working with his youth group again for the next few days. I figure after his comments on the baby formula he's bound to have an opinion on the subject. And what a great excuse for a long conversation with him!

## February 21, 1973

The whole group slept in this morning. We woke at 8:00 a.m., the time we were supposed to be at work! There was no sign of our mini-bus, so we dashed for public transport. Thank goodness Lise knew the name of the *kampung* where our project was. In the bus, we joked with her that since she was "Mom" she should be up early making our breakfast and then waking us. "Hah," she said, "what

145

do you take me for—a rug?" Well, she said it in French, *tapis*. Then we got a lecture on Women's Lib and how mothers are the first people on the planet who need to be liberated as they are *everybody's* slaves. Needless to say, we regretted the joke.

When we reached our project site, a fishing *kampung* near the coast, Ahmed's group were already at work with the villagers. The job involved clearing brush and picking up refuse on a nearby beach. It was a clean-up day for the whole village, organized by their youth brigade. Whenever a youth group wants help with a project, they call up the national executive, and other groups come out to support them. (Teenagers don't have time to get bored here. They're all too busy doing sports, work projects, and cultural and religious activities!)

The villagers came out as well as the youth, mainly to meet the "Europeans," I think—the usual wiry old men and women, plump mothers with their babies, and little kids running everywhere. There was a lot of laughing and joking of course. At break-time we ate what was on the side of the road, fresh coconut from the trees and loads of bananas. The village women also brought sticky rice wrapped in leaves and crisp slices of pineapple.

Males and females worked together as this wasn't a social affair. I managed to move over towards Ahmed and we worked side by side, our *parangs* slashing though *belukar*. The pungent green smell of cut grass and brush filled our noses. He wore his sarong and a white T-shirt. I was wearing a faded *baju kurong* that Rosnah gave me for work. They're cooler than jeans as the loose folds let your skin breathe and don't make you sweaty. I also wore a kerchief to keep my hair out of the way and to shade me from the sun. When I first walked over to Ahmed he seemed to stiffen with surprise, then he smiled his usual hello and introduced me to his team. I realized later that I had copied the women in Atas Tol, the way they wore their kerchiefs tied under the chin and all their hair tucked in. Did he think, just for a second, that I was a Malay girl with my kerchief, dark eyes, tanned skin and long dress?

He listened gravely when I told him about the groups which had broken up and the reasons why the group leaders and participants left the project. Eventually he stopped working altogether, lost in thought. I stopped, too, and we sat down at the side of the road, under a palm tree.

"I am sorry these young people and their youth leaders thought this way. Have we not decided for ourselves to invite you into our country and into our lives? Yet I know this concern, about outside influences on our society. Many Muslims, especially the older ones, fear the corrupting influence of the West which they see to be in moral decline. But I have such faith in Islam that I expect the opposite to be true. *Insha Allah*, it is we who shall influence the world."

I have to say I felt much better after that talk and less concerned by the notion that I shouldn't be here. Ahmed reminds me of the faith I used to have which I seem to have lost since I "grew up." He's three years older than me yet he believes totally in God. If there's one big difference between him and me, it's his fearlessness. Though he has a lot of responsibilities, he doesn't really worry about things. I've been thinking about that. Maybe I'd have more courage to do the things I want to do, if I left the final results in the hands of Someone Else.

In the afternoon we cleaned up the beach. Some of the fishermen were coming in from work. Wearing old sarongs, and bare-chested, they looked very thin, you could count their ribs. None of them spoke English, a lot were missing teeth, but they laughed and made jokes and took us for rides in their boats. Most were rowed by hand, though one had an outboard motor. Katie ordered us not to get tangled in the fishing nets and ruin someone's livelihood. She told the men in our boat that her dad was a fisherman and they were very excited and surprised. They think all Westerners are rich, not people who work for a living like they do. As we moved slowly from shore over the blue-green waves, I looked back at the beach with its shining white sand and wavering palm trees. A tropical paradise. That people actually live in these places the rest of us dream about!

## February 23, 1973

*T*oday was my last day working with Ahmed as we are leaving Terengganu tomorrow. It was the worst day of my life. I had hoped to be on his team or working near him, but there were two separate projects, one heavy labour and one light, which meant males and females were divided; the men to fell trees, the women to hoe fields. Again, at lunch, it was impossible to get near him as the men and women ate separately. I felt as if I were in one of those nightmares where you keep trying to approach someone but they disappear into a crowd and the closer you move, the further away they get. I gave up in the end since I was torturing myself. I worked alone, hoeing the dry soil, my kerchief over my head. Through the blur of tears I watched the dirt fall on my sandals and cling to the edge of my skirt.

At the end of the workday, the men built a bonfire to burn the last of the debris and brush. We gathered at the fire—the villagers, the youth groups and us—to sing the Malaysian national song.

*Rasa sayang hey*
*Rasa sayang sayang hey*
*Hey lihat nona jaur*
*Rasa sayang sayang hey*

A pining feeling, hey
What a pity,
To see the maiden only from afar
What a pity, hey.

That's when Ahmed came over to me and I was surprised and hurt to see that he was smiling. His face was lit up by the flames of the bonfire. Those dark eyes gleamed like ebony. I didn't try to hide my feelings. He shook his head gently and smiled again, that amazing, stunning, otherworldly smile.

"Do not be sad, my sister. Meeting and parting are a gift from God. *Insha Allah*, we shall meet again. I trust we shall."

He stood there waving to me as our bus pulled away, still smiling.

Back at home, our day's work done, we headed off to the beach with all our town pals. Mah, Dah, Zah, Zimi and Rosnah accompanied the girls and the one hundred Muhammeds headed off with the guys. At first we walked along the edges of the surf. The sunlit blues and greens of the water were exquisite to the eye. I've never seen beaches like the beaches of Terengganu, not even in the best travel posters. *Chendering*. I'll never forget that magical name, that magical place. Silver sand, turquoise sea, and tall stately palms. My own secret lagoon tucked away forever in the corner of my mind.

Then we decided to go swimming and things got a bit odd. All the Malay guys had bathing suits and they swam with us, but none of the girls did. Not one of them! (They couldn't all have been having their periods.) They just giggled and wouldn't answer when we asked if they were coming in. I can't believe we were so insensitive, but it was the first time we had come up against a cultural prohibition. It finally dawned on us that maybe they couldn't or wouldn't uncover themselves in public. They did paddle in the water and at one point Rosnah jumped right in and soaked her sarong, which of course dried in minutes. We (the Canadian girls) eventually grew aware that our friends were uneasy with us in bathing suits, even though we're talking seriously conservative one-piece numbers here. Anyway, we got dressed and copied the Malay girls by splashing and paddling in the shallows. Katie strolled along holding Dah's hand and I strolled along holding Rosnah's.

Something just occurred to me while I'm writing this. If Ahmed had been there, I wouldn't have gone swimming! I would have felt too naked in my bathing suit. That is really weird. And funny thing too, I wouldn't have been comfortable seeing him in a bathing suit either. But something tells me he would have kept his sarong on. The other guys are townies. Ahmed, being a country boy, is more conservative.

But do I want these feelings? Is this shame or modesty? I mean, swimming is such a wonderful thing, such a joy and delight. How could one swim properly, all covered up?

This evening we had a farewell dinner in a *restoran* downtown and invited all our pals. We insisted on treating them, which wasn't easy at all, and we're still not sure if we didn't upset some code of Malaysian hospitality. They kept saying that we were guests in their country. Katie retaliated with a Newfie—oops, Newfoundlander—saying, "Guests, like fish, stink after three days." Rosnah's father had given her the money to take us all to the movies and we only accepted on condition that we pay for dinner.

The movie! It was an Indonesian film about a woman who had a child out of wedlock, became a prostitute and sent her earnings to her son's adopted parents so they could educate him to be a doctor. He never knew who his real mother was. When she was dying, he was the doctor who came to look after her because he was a kind man who treated prostitutes when other doctors wouldn't. She knew who he was though, and he developed a special love for her. She even told him she had a son somewhere and he kept urging her to contact him! She died happily in his arms without telling him the truth and he wept over her.

Needless to say, we all bawled our eyes out. Serious sob-city.

I was glad all the gang came to say goodbye. It was really important to me to be out with friends and to be doing things. All the time I was laughing and talking, I was ignoring the terrible dark feeling inside. *Farewell Terengganu. Farewell Ahmed.*

The house is quiet tonight. Everyone is sleeping. I can

hear Katie's breath rising and falling like a soft wind. I am writing by the little lamp on my bedside table. Tears fall slowly onto these pages. It's typical, I guess. He has all the faith in the world and here I am, weeping in the dark.

February 23, 1973
Val's apartment, Kuala Lumpur!!!

*I*'m lying here in bed in Val's spare room, doctor's orders, still wondering what happened to me. This is the end result of a nightmare that began on Saturday when we went to Penang for "rest and relaxation." It seems that as soon as I left the warm embrace of Terengganu, everything started to go wrong.

We were given a break, a weekend off with no schedule or official functions. And what a place to have a holiday! Pulau Penang is the most beautiful island imaginable, even in a country which is another word for beauty. "The Jewel of the Orient," it's called. We quickly turned into maniac tourists and spent the day rushing around seeing all the sights. I'll never forget that giant golden Buddha reclining the full length of a house, and the snake temple with vipers crawling over the altars.

It was the first time we came across crowds of tourists and I found it disturbing. All that fatty white flesh! North Americans are the worst, while Europeans (the real ones), mostly British and Dutch, are less loud and vulgar. I can't count the number of women I met walking around the streets with a sarong tied above their chests and nothing else. This is how Malaysians dress for a shower! I even saw one woman wearing the top of a *baju kurong* without the skirt. Sure it comes to the knee, but you don't wear half an outfit. It must be so shocking for Malays to see it. And there were men in sarongs too, with no shirt on, their beer bellies hanging over the knotted part. Gross! But I wonder—would I have noticed these things if I hadn't spent two months living with Malaysians?

We were billeted in a small hotel in Georgetown, the capital of Penang. It was Western-style, with television sets in each room and bathrooms with a full-size bath. I admit it, I was delighted. Katie and I shared a room (of course) and we jumped on the beds, turned the TV up full blast and flipped a coin for who got the first bath. Plus we had room service. Katie ordered a bottle of gin with tonic and a lemon. She really misses booze sometimes and talks about her favourite Newfoundland drink called Screech. (I can only imagine what a drink with a name like that could do to you.) Then we ordered dinner in our room—steak and baked potatoes with sour cream—and sat and watched a movie, *The Seventh Dawn*, with William Holden. It's set in Malaysia and was filmed here, so it gets put on a lot. Oh gawd, that part when he told the English girl who was in love with him that the Malay word for virginity was "folded sarong" and then he put his hands on her shoulders and said—in a dead serious voice—"stay folded, sarong." We fell off the bed, laughing and hiccuping, till tears ran down our faces.

Later that night the whole gang went out on the town. Everyone dressed up in party clothes, the girls with loads of make-up on. Katie was pretty tight having finished the gin. Darren came around earlier to help her drink it and, I couldn't believe it, they went off in a trishaw together necking in public. I was disgusted at first but then I had to accept that Katie's done really well not smoking and drinking for so long, plus no sex. At the disco, I had two beers and even took a puff of a cigarette to prove to myself that I wasn't a total goody-two-shoes. There was a big crowd of us. A few Dutch guys on a business convention joined us, and an American couple on their honeymoon. Georgetown really hops at night (not like K.T. which was very quiet) with night clubs, cinemas, cocktail lounges and discos.

The floor show came on, girls in skimpy sequinned outfits with huge coloured fans and feathers. It wasn't striptease, but almost. An awful thing happened, then. I was taking another puff of Katie's cigarette, with my glass of beer in the other hand, when I glanced over at the door and my heart stopped. Ahmed stood there. With the bright hallway behind him, his face was lost in shadow like an eclipse. I suddenly saw myself as he must see me—face painted, my short dress, a cigarette in my mouth and alcohol in my hand, surrounded by drunken Westerners and half-naked women on stage.

I wanted to die. I wanted the ground to open up and swallow me. I was so ashamed. To be caught out. The real me.

Then, of course, I saw it wasn't him. A Malay guy his age, with the same dark hair and eyes, the same lean features, went over to the bar to get a tray of drinks for the restaurant downstairs.

I couldn't stay there a minute longer. Ignoring the protests of the others, I left by myself and got a trishaw home. The sparkling lights of the city blurred into a multi-coloured snake as the tears fell down my face. I had turned my back on him. So quickly, so easily. I had betrayed him. Betrayed my love for him and for his country. Everything he stood for, everything I had learned and experienced—Malaysian culture, Islamic values, a gracious way of living—I had traded these in for the shabby baubles of a loud and vulgar way of being. Cheap perfume, lipstick, cigarette ash and beer. Is this freedom?

When I got back to the hotel I was violently ill. I vomited everything up, steak and potatoes and beer. I went to bed with a splitting headache and a sore throat.

The next day, yesterday, is a muddle in my mind. I woke up really ill. At first Katie thought I had a whopper of a hangover like herself—she looked as bad as me, pasty-faced, bleary-eyed, and moaning for water—but then she crawled out of bed.

"Hey, kiddo, you only had a couple of beers."

She felt my forehead and went running for Lise. There were phone calls and a doctor came. He said I had a virus but it was complicated with an infection, possibly bladder or kidneys or both. He gave me a prescription for antibiotics but wanted tests done for the kidneys as it could be dangerous. He wanted to sign me into the hospital for tests the next day.

"We can't. She would be here on her own," Lise said. "We're leaving for a work project in Johor first thing in the morning."

Lise rang Val and he told her to send me down to K.L., that he would look after me. So I was packed onto a bus with a bottle of cooled boiled water. Katie kept insisting that she should go with me, but I refused. I didn't want company. The truth is I wanted to get away from all of them. A beautiful Indian woman sat beside me on the bus and she spread tiger balm on my forehead when she saw I was ill. She wore a sky-blue sari, her glass bracelets tinkled, and she smelled of rose-water. I was feverish and kept asking her was she an angel.

Val met me at the bus station and drove me to his apartment. I was surprised to find a bunch of kids hanging around. They had dropped out of their groups and were skipping whatever project they were supposed to be doing. What does this programme mean to them? I really couldn't believe their attitude. I mean, are they here to experience Malaysia and learn something or are they just along for the free ride?

I'm exhausted writing this, but I'm so bored lying here. Val brought his television in for me to watch but Malaysian soaps are as bad as Canadian ones and as usual no one can act. I think I'll take a nap. The antibiotics are really knocking me out.

## February 27, 1973

Val took me to the clinic this morning. The doctor didn't think culture tests were necessary after all, but he said the infection had spread rapidly, hence the headaches, fever, earache, sore throat, nausea and diarrhea (I'm a mess). More pills and if I'm no better in three days I have to go into hospital!

When we got back, Val had an argument with two of the guys. They wanted him to reimburse them for the money they had spent while on their own in Kuching. They had dropped out of their group's activities and stayed in the town instead of going on to the Sarawak work projects. I had no idea so many people were wandering around, doing their own thing! I asked them what the hell were they up to? They said they wanted to discover Malaysia "as individuals" since "the group thing was interfering with their direct experience."

"Then why didn't you pay as an individual and come by yourself?" I demanded, real sarcastic (felt like Katie).

I told them they were a bunch of spoiled white kids wanting everything their own way as usual, not giving a damn about anyone else or the effects their actions might have on the project. Boy, was I pissed off. Boy, did I give them hell.

Then Val announced that since I was sick and needed peace and quiet, everyone would have to return to their groups. Much as they didn't like it, he drove them all to the bus station. Later, when he came back and brought me in some Chinese tea, I asked him why *he* didn't give them shit. He said he didn't want to be too hard on anyone, that this experience is a difficult one and he couldn't expect everyone to make it, as if they were to pass a test or meet some standard of success. There was no way the programme could measure how much people learned or how much they had changed. As long as they were willing to stay in Malaysia and keep attempting the experience, he felt we were winning.

What an understanding guy.

February 28, 1973

*A* letter came today, from Katie to Val. God knows what's happening in Johor but it doesn't sound good. She was giving out hell about how it was impossible to live with a bunch of completely mismatched people while at the same time trying to assimilate into a new culture. The whole idea of the project was wrong, she wrote, and the participants should be adopted into families and "forget all the Western group-interaction bullshit." She went to town on everything, group leaders, the programme, schedules, official functions, the lot. Val showed it to me as Katie had put a P.S. on the bottom *pour moi*. But what a letter, I mean, total explosion city. They must be going cats and dogs at each other down there.

"Glad I'm not in Johor," I said to Val.

He said he liked the letter because Katie was letting off steam at the programme's authority figure—himself—and she didn't once complain about the Malaysians. He called her "the Irish letter-bomber" and said her fire came out loud and clear. Then he sat down and wrote her a long letter back; about the ideals of the programme and how it was always harder to work with others than by oneself which is why greed and capitalism often win out over sharing and co-operation. It was the easier way out but, in the end, it was never the best for humanity. He told her she was wonderful, to keep up the good work, *bon courage*, no surrender and he called her "one of the indomitable Irishry" (from an Irish poet called Yeats, apparently. Val is a brain). He promised he would take her out drinking at the end of the project and get her "lashed."

I asked him again, didn't it upset him, all this flak directed at him?

"That's what I get paid for," he shrugged. But then he was serious. "It's only when they go quiet that I worry. The ones who left didn't complain enough, didn't get their fears out in the open where we could have dealt with them. As long as you're all out there acting and reacting and expressing how you feel, I know the programme is up and running."

"Do you think Katie might leave?" I asked worriedly. I mean, she was tearing the project to shreds.

"Nah. Newfies are a hardy breed. They never give up. I'd say she's missing you. You're her best friend, aren't you?"

"Yes," I said proudly. Then I told him he better say "Newfoundlander" not "Newfie" when Katie was around.

"Thanks for the tip."

Most of today I spent in bed, sleeping on and off, wiped out by the pills. I could hear Val puttering about, working on his typewriter, or talking on the phone. He's so kind. He would tiptoe into my room, fill up the jug of iced water at my bedside and leave out fruit and *ketupat* (rice cake) to eat. In the afternoon, I sat up for a while, feeling refreshed. The sun was shining into the room, even with the curtains closed, and it was warm and bright. Val brought in some mail for me. Both Daniel and Matt wrote! I was stunned. I've never gotten letters from either of them in my life. They were short notes but the very act of their writing and saying they missed me brought tears to my eyes. The floodgates opened once I got started, I guess because I was sick and feeling low. Val held my hand while I blubbered away, talking about my family, my mom and dad, Gran, my brothers, how things were very strict but still it was a good

159

home, stuff like that. He didn't try to stop me from crying and kept saying quietly, "That's right, let it all out, have a good cry." (He's a kids' shrink at home. No doubt the best.) That's when he gave me Katie's letter to read. I guess he knew it would cheer me up, all that fire and brimstone. He sat on my bed and wrote his letter back to her, chatting away about the group and the project. I finally got up the nerve to ask him if he was a communist, when he wrote the bit about capitalism. While I'm getting more open-minded, I was relieved all the same when he said he wasn't.

"There are areas where I agree with communism, philosophically and economically, but the Soviet Union has put me off the idea as a reality. I couldn't possibly accept what they've done, what they're doing, to my homeland. And if Poland wasn't bad enough, when the tanks rolled into Czechoslovakia that proved for me they are no different than any other imperialist power. They are basically Russian pretending they are Soviet. I'm really an anarchist at heart, but I call myself a socialist. I'm an active member of the NDP and that's as red as I get."

At supper-time, I felt I could get up for a while. Val had made spaghetti with meat sauce and a salad and I managed to eat a bit of both. It was during dessert when he looked over at me quizzically and asked casually:

"Is there any particular reason why the President of the National Federation of Islamic Youth is calling me every day for an update on your condition?"

I was eating ice-cream and my spoon dropped into the bowl with a clatter.

"He phoned?! When? How did he know? You should have woken me!"

160

Val's eyebrows shot up into his receding hairline and I was suddenly aware how loud and excited I sounded. I went red as a beet and shut up.

"Ah," he said.

He was lost in thought for a minute. I didn't know what to say.

Then he murmured to himself, "A Scots Presbyterian from Calabogie and a Malay Muslim from Terengganu. Yes, it fits."

I thought he was being sarcastic, or maybe I was feeling defensive, but I got huffy and spoke in a cold voice:

"We have a lot in common."

"That's what I meant," Val said gently. "The outside is different, the form as it were. But at the heart, at the essence, where it matters, where we are who we are—yes, you would have a lot in common, you two."

"He's the most wonderful person I have ever met," I declared.

That's when I caught the look on Val's face. The same look that Ahmed's mother had given me. Sadness and sympathy. It made me want to shout at him, "It's not impossible! We'll find a way!"


March 1, 1973

*A*hmed came to visit me today. It was very awkward at first. He was wearing the clothes he wears at university, the Malaysian uniform for men, as I think of it. It's a kind of military summer suit, light trousers matching a short-sleeved shirt with epaulettes on the shoulders and pockets. I had got used to him in a sarong and now he looked so official. President of the National Federation of Islamic Youth. Still gorgeous, though. He had come from classes and carried books under his arm. One hand cradled the books, the other kept running through the thick dark hair at his forehead. You could tell he was ambivalent about the meeting; he wanted to be there to make sure I was okay, but he was uncertain about whether or not it was right. I felt sorry for him. It was probably the first time in his life that he was so unsure of himself.

Val made us Malaysian-style tea with lots of milk and sugar, served up with chocolate-chip cookies. Though he had planned to go shopping, he stayed in the apartment the whole time. He knew as well as I did that Ahmed would leave if the two of us were alone without a chaperone. Val must have picked up on Ahmed's discomfort because he went on for some time about how well the project was going and how individual friendships were a sign of that success, since they could only have untold beneficial effects for inter-racial, inter-cultural and inter-religious relations. Val kept looking at both of us as he said this and I could feel his approval sheltering us from doubt and fear. Ahmed relaxed visibly at this approval, partly I think because it came from an official source, but more so because he recognized the truth of what Val was saying. For a moment I caught a glimpse of it too, the full implications of what he meant, though it was a sad glimpse and not what I wanted to see. Someday I would tell my children about my dear friend, Ahmed, even as he would tell his children about me, and in the way that only good can, the ripple of love and tolerance could affect generations.

Ahmed talked briefly about his studies—history, religion, sciences, Arabic literature. He intends to be a teacher. I told him about my plans to be a journalist. Val eventually excused himself to make phone calls in his office, but he left his door open in deference to the situation. Both Ahmed and I were quite relaxed by that time.

"How did you know I was sick?" I asked.

"I had called your accommodation in Johor. It was presumptuous of me, perhaps, but I knew your itinerary as all the youth leaders have copies to help co-ordinate the project. I was phoning to ask how you were and to tell you my good news, Jessie-cah. But then your friend, Katie, told me you were ill and staying here. I contacted your co-ordinator as soon as I heard. I was very concerned."

"That was kind of you," I said. "I would have done the same if I had heard you were ill."

We were smiling at each other. It was enough, for the moment, to be meeting again. Nothing else mattered. It was heaven.

"What's the good news?" I asked.

"My Aunt Noor-Hayati, who lives in Kota Kinabalu in Sabah, has written to my mother asking that I come and visit. Her son, my cousin, is coming home from England where he is studying medicine, and she wants me to keep him company. It is good fortune, Jessie-cah, but that means I shall be in Borneo when you are."

My eyes must have been huge. I was suddenly overwhelmed by the fact that the universe was helping us out, bringing us together. It filled me with hope and a sense that our love was meant to be.

"It's a gift from God," I whispered.

"Yes, I believe so," Ahmed said quietly. "We have much to be grateful for, Jessie-cah."

Then he took one of his books and handed it to me.

"I do not wish to counter your own beliefs. I know you are a devout Christian and it is written in the Holy Book, '*Recognize with justice those who are sincere and humble, though they may be themselves not of your flock, if they witness to Truth.*' But you have expressed an interest in Islam and this is the heart and soul of Islam. I thought you would like to read it."

It was a bound copy of the Qur'an, with Arabic script on one side of the page and an English translation on the other. I was overcome by the gift and so delighted to receive it. I knew that Ahmed was offering me a part of himself.

"*Allahu Akbar,*" I said. "Thank you, my brother."

## March 3, 1973

*I* am crossing the South China Sea on my way to Borneo. Wow, that looks amazing written down.

We set sail from Singapore yesterday afternoon on a passenger and cargo ship called the *Rajah Brooke*, named after James Brooke, the White Rajah, an English adventurer who ruled Sarawak before it became a British colony. It sounds romantic, but the reality sure ain't. What a shock we got when we discovered we were travelling third-class in the hold, or The Hole as we call it, the dirty, dank, smelly underbelly of the boat! The bunks are planks of wood hanging by chains from the ceiling. The food is awful, pure swill—the same rice, fish and cabbage boiled together for breakfast, lunch and supper. Mind you, it's free but, hey, pay me to eat it.

"*Nous sommes dans le Bastille!*" wailed Louise.

I was part of the general outcry myself, furious that the Canadian government was so cheap that they wouldn't even buy us decent tickets to travel. Surprisingly, Katie didn't complain at all.

"Smells like home," she said, climbing onto her bunk. "Fish-heads and diesel."

Katie announced that the only way to survive the experience was to get drunk and stay drunk, so off she went to spend all her money on warm beer from the third-class "bar,"—crates set up by the crew near the kitchen galley. She was blissfully out of her brain all day yesterday and passed out early last night. Lise did manage to calm us down by pointing out that we were not tourists and that we were here to experience Malaysian life on all levels. This is how poor Malaysians travel, especially the indigenous people of Borneo. Well, that was brought home to me when a Dyak man picked the bunk right next to me!

He's smaller than your average Malay and even finer-boned. Bare-chested, with beads around his neck, he wears black trousers and sandals and a woven hat with feathers. His arms are covered in tattoos like black lace and his ear lobes reach down to his shoulders!!! I try not to stare, but in fact we both stare at each other, all agog. He seems as surprised and baffled by me as I am by him. I don't think white people travel third-class (there's a few up in first) and perhaps he's never been so close to one, especially a female? I wish we could talk, but it's like we don't belong in the same space or time. Whenever I try to catch his eye to say

165

hello, he ducks his head and pretends I'm not here. He looks so strange and wonderful to me, like someone from the past who still lives in the present.

How must I look to him? A big white fish? That's what they call Wyn Sargent, the American woman who married a Dyak chief. *We are not to mention her.* Serious orders from above. She's a taboo subject. But Dave found an article about her in *The Straits Times* and we all devoured it. There was a photo of this tall, black-haired woman, heavy-boned with a big toothy smile. Beside her stood a little native man with a toothless grin. Apparently she's a journalist and she's travelling with her young son through the interior of Borneo. She's in the part that belongs to Indonesia, whereas we are going to Sarawak and Sabah which belong to Malaysia (they are called "East Malaysia"). Politics in Borneo seem more fraught than on the mainland. Sarawak is divided into military districts and there's a war going on with communist insurgents in the jungles. The American Peace Corps were thrown out over some incident, though again we don't know what happened nor can we ask questions. For the sake of our project we cannot be political.

But we'll be meeting the native people ourselves when we stay in their longhouses. I can't wait. Apparently Borneo wasn't part of the original plans for the project, but the Malaysian government want to include the indigenous peoples in their social programmes and we fall into that category! It will be more like a cultural visit they told us, though we are expected to do some work as well.

Last night, Louise and I tried to sneak into the first-class bathrooms to take a shower, but the steward caught us and threw us out, yelling and cursing in Chinese. We had to return to our own shower room, worst luck. It's like a boiler room with one running tap of freezing cold water. The crew kept peeking in through cracks and holes in the walls, and under the door. Thank goodness we wore sarongs.

I'm up on deck right now, near the life-boats, where third-class passengers can go for a breath of fresh air. There's a pile of crates in front of me bound for Australia. The open sea and salt breezes are reviving me. Only one more night to endure. We arrive in Kuching tomorrow. I'm thinking about Ahmed, of course. There's an ache inside, pining away quietly just to see his face and hear his voice. This ship takes me nearer to the time and place where we'll meet. I nearly died when Val said he wanted me to skip Sarawak altogether. My infection hasn't completely cleared up and I still look pale, with dark circles under my eyes. He was worried I wouldn't be well enough for the trip (this boat makes me wonder if he wasn't right) and offered me a job as his personal assistant, to stay in K.L. and do paperwork for the programme. No way baby!!! I'm not taking a desk job, not while the rest of my gang are adventuring in Borneo and my true love awaits me. I practically got hysterical and threatened to run away and join my group. Val found this hilarious as it was the opposite of what other kids were always threatening to do.

In the end he drove me from K.L. to join the guys in Singapore. It was so great to see them again. Katie and I went crazy. It's only when we get separated that I realize how much I love that little chicken-legged kid. Ray gave me a hug and a kiss and so did Darren. (Yeah, I actually got a smacker on the lips and put that into the memory album. One from Mr. Hunk of the Year.) Lise, Louise, Claude and

167

Cyn also hugged me to death and Dave shook my hand with a warm but ever-so-polite "delighted to see you back in the fold." An earthquake wouldn't move that boy.

The project in Johor went fine after all, and as it turned out, the only fight was between Katie and the girls in the group. She's giving them the cold shoulder right now, won't even look at them and refuses to talk to them. Apparently it started late at night in the girls' room. They were in a *kampung* house, pretty cramped quarters, all the girls in one small room and all the guys in another. Katie went drinking with Darren and came home late and woke the others up. They held a constructive criticism session with her the next day. Katie's not the best with criticism anyway, she always takes it as a personal attack whether founded or not, but it was just too much for her, all of them ganging up at once. She took it silently, but when they asked for her response she said, "Why don't you all go and fuck yourselves." And that was that. But she's talking to the guys of course.

Later, same day:

I decided to go looking for Katie. I was worried about her as she looked pretty green this morning. She's fine. She and Darren (are they spending a lot of time together or what?) were befriended by some of the crew who took them into their cabin. I got invited too. The cabins are small, four men to each, but clean and neat with portholes letting in air and light. Katie and Darren were drinking whisky with two guys, one of whom turned out to be the cook. "Food no good, huh?" he said with a big guffaw. Then he went off to get us some fresh rice, barbecued pork and sweet tea. Yum. All the crew are great, not counting the shower episode. They're Chinese sailors but most speak English from travelling around the world. They play mah-jong a lot and one guy tells fortunes. (I'll be married in three years to a very rich man. Tell me another one.) They said we should go to Bali which is "paradise on earth." They also said "hippies" go third-class, usually Australian or American, but they rarely see women in the hold.


March 7, 1973
My sister Asmah's house in Miri, Sarawak

*I* can't sleep tonight, I'm too nervous and excited. Tomorrow we visit the longhouses of the native peoples of Borneo. When we were in Kuching we saw exhibits about them in the Sarawak Museum and I wrote down the names of some of the tribes: Iban, Bidayuh (hill people), Kayan, Kenyah, Kelabit (settled farmers), Murut (related to Kelabit), Kadazan, Punan (wandering people who live off the jungle), Melanau (fisherfolk), land Dyak and sea Dyak (depending on where they live). The displays of woven baskets, huge totem poles, canoes and wood carvings were so like North American native artifacts. Could they be related?

Asmah just turned in her sleep but thankfully the lamplight didn't wake her. It's late and I should be in bed too but I'm fed up tossing and turning and hugging the bolster. All the night creatures of the countryside are singing through the open window. The sweet scent of burning wood wafts on a warm breeze. I've been very happy here in Miri.

My family is wonderful. I've grown particularly close to Haji Derus and his daughter, Hajia Asmah Derus, who is the same age as me. (They've both been to Mecca.) They live in a big *kampung* house on the outskirts of town, surrounded by fields. Everything seems so easygoing and cheerful here. Haji Derus is a prosperous farmer with two kids. Asmah's older brother, Rashid, goes to the university of K.L. He was polite when he met me, but didn't stay to talk as he was dressed in whites to play a cricket match. I got the impression he felt he was too old to chat to his younger sister's friends, which reminded me exactly of Matthew (the way he's polite but condescending to Shirley who has a crush on him). It's been great making friends with Asmah as she is my first real counterpart in Malaysia. She's the same age, has the same amount of education, plans to go to university, and in many ways leads the same kind of life as me. In fact, her mom and dad remind me of mine. Haji Derus is a kind and gentle man who dotes on his daughter. He won't arrange a marriage until she agrees. Asmah's mom is the old-fashioned wife and mother, always busy with her housework, but she also spends a lot of time visiting her sisters and mother who live up the road. I just realized something. While I'm saying that Haji Derus reminds me of Dad, he's also a perfect example of what Ahmed will be like when he's older! I came all the way to South-East Asia to fall in love with a man like my father?!

I told Asmah about Ahmed this evening, as we sat on the veranda and talked about life. She asked straight out if I would like to marry him and stay in Malaysia. I was taken by surprise. I nearly choked. To have it stated so simply and openly. My secret dream, my silent hope, what I want most in the world and yet cannot bring myself to face. My heart cried out, "Yes! yes!" and she could see it in my eyes and in the flush of colour and the confusion it caused as I stammered helplessly.

"You could become Muslim and stay here, yes?" she said matter-of-factly.

And that was it in a nutshell. The thing I have not wrestled with because it might defeat me. I mean, I respect Islam so much. How could I not, from what I've learned and seen in the lives of my friends? But it is not my path. I've never doubted my own religion for all that I object to Mom and Dad's strictures from time to time. I've never doubted that the Bible is the word of God and Jesus, his son. As for living in Malaysia, it's a wonderful country but I don't belong here. I want to visit other countries and maybe stay in them a while, but Canada is my home. I'm a true-blue Canadian.

I explained all of this to Asmah as we sipped cups of tea and watched the sun set. She shook her head, bemused.

"You are different from Malay girls this way. Once I marry, I will do as my husband does, I will go where he goes."

"But would you marry a man who isn't a Muslim?" I asked.

"Marry an unbeliever?" She was aghast. "That is unthinkable."

Asmah's eyes widened and then she nodded, finally recognizing the gulf between Ahmed and myself. We changed the subject after that, but what I left unsaid I will write here now. I refuse to believe that our love is hopeless. What God has put together, the world cannot keep apart.

March 12, 1973
Rumah Bulan Ding—Longhouse of the Half-Moon

*A*t last, a moment to write about this utterly incredible
unimaginable totally mind-blowing experience!!! For
the past five days—it seems like aeons in a place beyond
time—we've been travelling through the heart of Sarawak,
journeying upriver into the interior, staying a night here
and a day there at different longhouses. Coming to
Malaysia was amazing in itself, but this is something else
altogether. The life and breath of the jungle. The men,
women and children who belong to the rainforest. The
tribes of people who were once the headhunters of Borneo!

Dyak words, some similar to Malay:
*datai*—come (*datang* in Malay)
*jalai*—go (*jalan* in Malay)
*makai*—eat (*makan* in Malay)
*pengidup*—life
*tuai rumah*—head man of the house (chief)

I'm sitting on the *ruai*, a great porch of bamboo poles
strung together which stretches the length of the house.
The house itself, built on stilts, is home to an entire village,
having twenty-one rooms or, as they say themselves,
"doors." (The biggest longhouse we visited had thirty-six
doors.) In front of me stretches a brown river where we
bathe in our sarongs. All around, as far as the eye can see, is
lush green jungle.

My head is aching from drinking *tuak*, though I didn't
have that much. I sip it as slowly as possible since it's

powerful stuff. It can either be clear or murky white, a drink they distil themselves, real-life moonshine. It's impolite not to accept it and I've heard rumours that if you don't take it voluntarily, they hold you down and pour it in. Needless to say, certain group members needed no encouragement and have been out of their skulls for the entire visit.

"It's like Screech!" screeched Katie as she guzzled it down. "No, even better, it's like the *poteen* Uncle Dermot brings over from Ireland!"

This is an Iban house we're staying in now. No drinking or partying for the moment, as everyone's at work. The men fish, while the women plant crops in a cleared space nearby. We're supposed to be helping, but we're all too exhausted and/or hung-over to move. We've been on the go continually, travelling upriver in a huge canoe called a longboat. We've journeyed through miles and miles of rainforest and jungle. Vines trailed from the trees and into the water like those old Tarzan movies I watched as a kid. There was always something slithering off the banks with a splash, but I never saw what. I kept an eye out for crocodiles and piranha, and spotted loads of snakes coiled on the branches of trees. It's never quiet in the jungle. All night and day, it sings; strange birds squawking, monkeys screeching, giant insects chirping. And then the gongs ring out, the only sound of human presence.

They ring to welcome us, as each time we arrive at a longhouse the whole village turns out. Some people wear traditional costume, red and yellow woven skirts decorated with silver ornaments. Most wear sarongs. Many have their ear lobes stretched to various lengths, even touching their shoulders, and also black tattoos on their arms, legs and chests. We are paraded up and down the long hall of the house, then we sit for a communal feast—rice cooked in bamboo, chicken and monkey meat, fruits and greens. After that, we dance all night till the early hours of morning.

I had to stop writing for a minute as I got a fit of laughing. The thought of last night, and me and Louise doing the Swallow Dance. The gongs were gonging away and all the Ibans were sitting on the floor in the common hall and waving at us to get up and dance. We all knew how, of course, as we've been dancing in every house. Louise jumped up and dragged me with her. Off we went, hopping around on one foot, flapping our arms like wings. The gongs went faster and faster and so did we, in crazy circles. The hall spun around in a blur of laughing faces. I nearly bounced off a pole but steadied myself, and despite laughing so much I stepped up my pace. Then, before I knew it, I tripped over my own feet and went flying head over heels into the crowd. Everyone howled. Iban fun.

We were all in party form as it was Dave's nineteenth birthday. Katie, me, Cyn and Louise put on bright red lipstick and kissed him hundreds of times till he was covered in red lip marks, even on his glasses. We wouldn't have done it anywhere else and everyone laughed, especially the Ibans. Poor old Dave. He's so shy, he nearly died, but you could tell he enjoyed it too, the fuss we made of him. The Head Man lent him a traditional costume, a woven loin cloth and a silver belt, with a hat of hornbill feathers and a shield and sword. After drinking a lot of *tuak*, Dave got into the swing of things and decided to dance. He copied the Chief who danced along with him, making quick moves like a hunter-warrior. Dave wasn't as graceful and his loin cloth kept flapping up to the squeals and giggles of the native women. Us too, of course. Then he really let go (so much for being a quiet guy), brandishing his sword with threatening gestures and hopping around like a madman, glasses falling off his nose, to the appreciation of all. Hey Dave, great birthday! Where's the party next year?

Even though Katie was quite drunk (or maybe because she was), she managed to dance for hours. She did the one where you turn and twist your hands and move in slow motion, down on your knees and back up again, then a few short hops. Birdlike movements, actually, as the hornbill is the sacred bird of the tribes of Borneo. She lasted so long, the Head Man put his cloak over her shoulders and his hat on her head. (I guess their symbols of authority aren't exclusive like ours.)

Oh gawd, the time Cyn and I were sitting together in the hall, playing with some little kids. We were putting their hair in pigtails. Suddenly I saw something black, at the corner of my eye, scoot over towards Cyn and up her sarong. She saw it too and froze. Her mouth opened to scream even as a woman ran towards her. The rapid-fire thump of bare feet on the boards was like a drum roll. The woman pulled Cyn to her feet, shook out her skirt, and out fell a spider the size of my hand! The woman stomped it to death. Cyn went white, but she closed her mouth without uttering a sound. The woman grinned and went back to her weaving. We went back to brushing the little girls' hair. Life in Sarawak.

In the last house, a Dutch priest came to put on a Roman service. I was surprised when he did a native dance in the middle of it. He was very graceful and wore a hat

175

with hornbill feathers. (I watched from the back. Katie, Lise, Claude and Louise attended the service.) He talked to us later about being a missionary to the tribes and how it was important to end their "slavery to superstition." He said their religion did them a lot of harm; for example, if a bird flew into a longhouse they would have to abandon the house because it was cursed. That could mean impoverishment for them if they had just planted crops or couldn't find a good place to settle in. Wow, the bad side of religion. I didn't say anything, but I wondered to myself if Roman Catholicism might not bring its own harmful superstitions to replace the old ones.

When I said this to Katie later, I expected her to accuse me of bigotry, but she laughed and said I should have spoken up. She would have enjoyed it. R.C.s are so strange. Their religion demands total obedience to what their priests say and yet all the ones I've met are so irreverent!

"How can you say one thing and do another?" I asked her.

"You're such a Prod," was her reply.

Oh yeah, one more thing I want to remember to tell Mom and Dad. One of the longhouses had a big framed picture hanging in their hall, above the jars of *tuak* and the brass gongs that are the sign of their wealth. It was an old black-and-white photograph of Queen Elizabeth and Prince Philip having a picnic with their kids in front of Balmoral Castle in Scotland. I kept staring at the picture of the Royal Family in kilts and tweeds, then back at the longhouse, the rattan mats and woven hangings, the toothless old people sitting in their doorways, the little kids running up and down the hall. Human beings are so weird.

March 13, 1973
Kota Kinabalu, the capital of Sabah

*M*ore memories of the longhouses demand to be written down but my heart is singing a different song. Tomorrow I will be reunited with Ahmed! There was a letter waiting for me when we arrived here. I phoned him at his aunt's immediately and we've arranged to have lunch in a *restoran* downtown. It was so wonderful to hear his voice. So wonderful to know I'll see him soon. I'm going to sort out my clothes to decide what I'll wear. The rest of the group have gone off to explore the city. Thank goodness we don't have to do anything here. We're in a government rest-house and we've been given time off to recover from the longhouses (badly needed). The day after tomorrow we're climbing Mount Kinabalu, the highest mountain in South-East Asia. That gives me a day to spend with Ahmed and perhaps we can arrange another meeting when I come down from the mountain. I want to read his letter again. To look at his writing, to think of him thinking of me. Not that he says much. Just that he's looking forward to seeing me. Sigh.

March 15, 1973
5,000 feet above sea level on Mt. Kinabalu, the sacred mountain of the Kadazan people

*S*o much to write about as always. I'm in a state of the purest ecstasy. Is it the rare air up here? Or the thought of Ahmed sleeping near me, in the next room with the rest of the guys? Hah! I can hardly believe that Fate has stepped

177

in once again to grant us more time together.

As it turned out, we only had a short meeting yesterday since Ahmed had to drive his cousin to the airport to fly back to England. But what could have been the biggest disappointment of my life—I had hoped we could spend the day together—turned out to be a blessing in disguise.

Lise and Claude had agreed to come along as chaperones, as I knew Ahmed would have been uncomfortable if we were alone. He had asked on the phone if some of my group would like to join us for lunch and I got the hint. I wore a scarf on my head, to honour him, and the pale yellow looked great with my green *baju kurong*. He didn't say anything, but I saw his eyes widen as he took in the scarf. His smile was gorgeous. We all sat together and ordered iced Milos and *rojak*, then sweet cakes for dessert.

Lise did most of the talking at first, as Ahmed directed his conversation mainly at her in recognition of her position as group leader. She knew a lot about his organization from official reports and thanked him for being so supportive of our project. Claude talked about the climb up Kinabalu and how everyone was looking forward to it, but he wondered if it would be difficult or not. Ahmed had actually climbed the mountain when he was younger, with a youth brigade, and he talked about the tricky bits on the rock face. He said some people mistook it for an easy climb because so many did it, but in fact there are dangerous ravines where one can get lost. That's when it happened. I couldn't have foreseen it and I nearly fell off my chair with shock and joy.

Lise asked Ahmed if he would consider accompanying us on the climb. Since we only had one guide, he would be of great assistance. OMIGOD. I nearly fainted. And

Ahmed's face, it was like the sun rising. His happiness was dazzling. You know, he's so innocent really. He didn't even try to hide his delight.

"I would be honoured to help you in any way possible," he said.

And that was that. Heaven on a plate.

Boy, do I owe Lise. She grinned and shrugged when I fell over myself later, thanking her profusely. She winked at Claude and I suddenly realized that the two of them had cooked up the scheme together. My group is so great. I love them to pieces.

And here we are, in a mountain hostel that looks so Canadian we all nearly died of homesickness. It's a chalet of stained wood with big airy rooms with bunk beds and sleeping bags. There's a large kitchen where we cook for ourselves. (Lise bought a load of groceries, tins of mackerel and beans, packaged noodles and fruit.) The dining area has an open fireplace like a ski lodge. The air up here is cool and dry, again like Canada in the early autumn. Some of the kids have decided that they won't climb the mountain after all. They want to hang out in the chalet and take walks around here. Katie, Darren, Ray, Lise and I have decided to go, with Godtol, our guide, and of course, my dear Ahmed. That's the mountaineering team. Here's hoping we make it to the top.

A hilarious note to all this. Would you believe it, the whole group had to go shopping in Kota Kinabalu for blue jeans since none of us had them, *except Ahmed.* That led to a lot of laughs. It's great to be in denims again, though they have a crease down each leg. Ugh. Ahmed grinned at me this evening when I came out for supper in jeans and a sweater, my hair in a braid down my back.

"Is this what you look like in Canada, Jessie-cah?"

I blushed furiously, because it was the first time he had made a direct comment on my appearance. For a moment I thought he was flirting with me, but then I realized he was teasing. That's Malay humour, of course. He looked really nice in jeans with a pullover. It was strange to see him that way. For the first time I was able to imagine him in Calabogie meeting my friends.

I must stop writing and get to sleep. We'll be up early tomorrow and I want all my strength for the climb. I'm determined to make it. So is Katie and Lise. Some army guys who had just come down from the mountain said the girls shouldn't go as they'd hold the guys back. We'll see about that.

## March 16, 1973

*I*'m writing this with freezing cold hands. The pen is shaking in my fingers. Though it's not yet dark outside, the others are asleep, resting up for the final climb tomorrow. We're in a small aluminum shack at the base of the peak. Only one of us dropped out—Darren. He had a fight with Katie on the way up. He wanted to wander off and fool around in the bushes. She wanted to climb the mountain. (Guess that's the end of that relationship.) I thought I was going to drop out myself at one point, but in the end I couldn't. When you're climbing a mountain, it's the most important thing in your life to get to the top. Anything else is failure.

We started out early this morning, going at a steady pace, all of us together with the guide. Godtol is a small man who carries a pack on his back the same size as himself. His face is dark and wizened but his eyes glitter like stars. He never speaks to us, except to Ahmed, and only then to give instructions. Ahmed says Godtol goes up the mountain three or four times a week, so it's old hat to him (!).

Eventually everyone moved at their own pace. Ray was the fastest with his long legs and he disappeared ahead. Darren and Katie were next to take off, but then they had their fight and Darren marched back to the hostel with his face like a storm. Katie caught up with Ray and finished the climb with him. They were both in their sleeping bags and fast asleep by the time the rest of us straggled into the shack. Lise stayed with the guide who kept a steady pace and, last but not least, came Ahmed and me. It wasn't deliberate, our climbing alone, we just liked stopping to look at things.

The wonders of Mt. Kinabalu! Waterfalls splashed through crevices in the rocks. The trees were loud with bright birds. Exotic flowers bloomed in the greenery, a hundred different kinds of orchid and the beautiful hibiscus, the national flower of Malaysia. We came upon loads of pitcher plants—they're so amazing! Big jug-shaped flowers that fill up with rainwater to drown the insects they digest for food. Ahmed told me about the *nepenthes raja*, a huge pitcher plant that holds up to four pints (!) but we didn't find one, too bad. At first Godtol came back to check on us, but I guess he decided we were fine in the end, as he left us alone.

The climb was easy at first and we strolled at a leisurely pace ever upwards. We joked and talked and even sang a few songs. "*Rasa Sayang Hey,*" of course, and I sang "The

Mountains and MaryAnn" for Ahmed which he liked. He said I had a lovely voice. Then things started to get difficult. The path grew steeper and was overgrown with vines and gnarled roots. We had to beat back the brush with sticks. The air got thinner the higher we climbed. I started to get short-winded and pant for breath. I thought my lungs would burst. Sometimes Ahmed reached back and grasped my hand to pull me up. That was the first time he ever touched me and I was too busy climbing to enjoy it!

We finally reached a place where there was a sign that said DANGER DO NOT GO BEYOND THIS POINT WITHOUT AN OFFICIAL GUIDE. But Godtol was nowhere to be seen. We decided we couldn't wait for him because our legs began to stiffen as soon as we stopped. A mist was settling over the mountain. Obviously the best thing to do was to keep going.

The fog moved in fast. Soon we could hardly see at all. After a few falls on slippery ground we knew we were on the rock face. I had seen this section of the mountain through the telescope at the chalet—a mass of sheer grey rock that goes straight to the peak. That was encouraging as it meant we were well on our way, but at the same time this was the most dangerous part of the climb and it was shrouded with mist!

We grabbed onto the ropes that hung down the rock. It was a gruelling ascent. Ahmed insisted on going behind me in case I fell. We actually couldn't see each other and called out at intervals to make sure we weren't lost. Sometimes a rope would end suddenly—when we reached the place where it was embedded in the rock—and I had to search around blindly with my hands to find the next one. There was one time when I panicked and couldn't find the rope. A scramble nearly had me tumbling down the rock face. I clawed my way up, even held onto a bit of root *with my teeth!*

It was wet and drizzly inside the fog but that wasn't the only thing that soaked my face. I wept quietly to myself, I felt so miserable. My body ached and I knew I would soon give up. And yet I continued, climbing like a robot: pull rope, push feet, slack rope and rest, pull rope, push feet, slack rope and rest. Finally I did cry out that I couldn't go any further. Ahmed said nothing, but when we reached a level place he called to me to stop. We sat down on what we figured was a boulder. Everything around us was milky white. We couldn't see a thing, not even the ground at our feet.

I don't know how long we sat there. I was crying quietly and Ahmed held my hand, murmuring quiet words to console me. I apologized for being weak and wondered what on earth we could do. I was sure I could go neither forward nor back.

Then, at last, the mist began to clear. Slowly at first, so that we could just make out shadowy shapes around us. And then it actually rolled away, as if the cloud had decided to run down the mountain. And what a sight! There, in front of us, rose a peak so huge it was as if a stone giant stood before us. It was immense and monstrous. We were tiny and insignificant. I felt as if I was falling over the edge of the world. Now I really started to bawl, out of shock and awe. Pure mountain madness.

Ahmed wept too as he stared up at the peak.

"*Allahu Akbar,*" he whispered. "We are so small before your work."

I looked back at the expanse of rock face we had climbed and I knew I would never have made it if I had seen where we were going. But it was easy to resume climbing after that. Funny how spirit or morale makes all the difference. Shining in the sunlight ahead of us, like a lighthouse, was the aluminum shack we are staying in tonight. We found the others here already. Lise was just getting into her sleeping bag.

Ahmed and I ate together, a tin of cold beans and bread and cheese. We didn't talk much and only in whispers so as not to disturb the rest. Yet even though I was exhausted and aching, I didn't want to go to sleep. I wanted to hold on to every moment with him. The two of us huddled together for warmth, our sleeping bags around our shoulders, closer to each other than we had ever been. Those dark-brown eyes gazed into mine with such serene joy. I thought I would die of happiness.

"You have great courage, Jessie-cah. I knew that Kinabalu would not defeat you."

Even as I'm writing this, I stop to glance over at him where he lies sleeping on the bottom bunk. His eyelashes rest on his smooth dark skin. My prince, my Arabian prince.

## March 17, 1973

Godtol woke us at about 4:00 a.m. in time to see a perfect moonrise. We groaned as we stretched our aching muscles. Outside the shack the air was cold and crisp. A few deep breaths, honey and oranges for energy, and we were off. To conquer the peak.

In the eerie light before dawn, we walked in a moonscape. Craters and jagged edges of rock. Grey sky and grey stone. Once again, the climbers separated. Ahmed and I went slowly together. Just as he had done yesterday, he occasionally reached out to take my hand to guide me over a steep or tricky part. I would clasp his wordlessly, in a shock of inner delight. His hand was dry and warm, neither smooth nor rough but a combination of both. I can't say how I felt. Perhaps it was the altitude but I could hardly breathe.

WE REACHED THE TOP.

And we stood above the world.

Lise and Ray were there with Godtol and they greeted us with yahoos and claps on the back. We laughed wildly and triumphantly, as if we were the team that had conquered Everest. I was just beginning to wonder what had happened to Katie when we heard someone calling below us. She had wandered off-course and was heading up the wrong peak when she spotted us. We waved her upwards and encouraged her with shouts. Her voice echoed over the stony landscape.

"*Beannachtai Padraig!*" she shouted and she kicked up her heels to do a jig. "Happy St. Patrick's Day!"

I'll never forget that crazy image of an Irish dancer on a mountain peak in Borneo.

By the time Katie reached us, a hush had fallen over all. We sat together, arms linked, and gazed in silence. Clouds sailed below us, white scarves of mist around the smaller peaks. In the far distance were the green hills and jungles of East Malaysia. Then the sun rose. We caught our breaths. The rocky valleys, the mountains, the grey stone landscape were afire with a red and orange glow. Who could have known such wonders existed? Who could have known such beauty would unfold before us?

I'm writing this in the chalet. We took our time to saunter back and everyone congratulated us. Too bad the army guys were gone. I would have loved them to see that the women had succeeded. Tomorrow we fly back to Kuala Lumpur. Ahmed left this afternoon, back to his aunt's in Kota Kinabalu. He looked very sad when he said goodbye but he'll be in K.L. in two days and he'll call me then. How desperately we snatch at the last particles of time. Five more days and I leave Malaysia. I don't want to know it. The other climbers kept saying, "What a way to end the project!" but I refused to agree or to echo their sentiments. I can't believe it's over. It's just not possible. A love like this can't end.

March 20, 1973
Good Ole Kampung Pandan

*O*ne more day and night in Malaysia. We leave Thursday morning. All the groups are back, with the last stragglers coming in today from Kedah. Everyone's happy to be going home. It's been a long and demanding experience. Some kids look a bit shell-shocked and we're much fewer in number. Only two groups, Betty's and ours, lost no members. There's a great sense of relief and also one of accomplishment, as we quietly congratulate ourselves for hanging in through thick and thin. Val made a speech at supper that made everyone feel great.

"I'm not into handing out gold stars or medals. This project is not a competition. But I want to say, 'Well done,' to each and every one of you. You have proved our ideals

186

and goals are possible. You have led the way."

It's obvious that I'm not in the same frame of mind as the others. I find it hard to join in the post-mortems, the late-night discussions on what was the best and the worst of the project. I just can't. I'm not ready to wrap it up. It's not over for me. Will it ever be? Sometimes I get this crazy idea that I'll hide when the bus comes. That I won't get on the airplane. I'll stay in Malaysia. But of course that's insane. It's not as if Ahmed has asked me to marry him. There hasn't even been talk of love for heaven's sake!

He's back from Sabah. He phoned me today and asked if he could take me and another group member on a tour of K.L. tomorrow. I raced around trying to get someone to chaperone us and was nearly hysterical with panic when I discovered that everyone was busy. Then Ray caught me by surprise by cancelling his own plans and agreeing to come.

"So you'll know there's no hard feelings," he said. "What are friends for?"

That made me cry. People are so kind.

Ahmed also mentioned coming to the airport with me. I push the thought out of my mind. I must think of something else. The pain is threatening to pull me apart.

I'll write about the last few days. We flew home from Sabah on Air Malaysia. That was a treat. A champagne flight with beautiful stewardesses and the best Malaysian cuisine. Plus free champagne. I had a glass to celebrate the climb up Kinabalu. It fizzed in my nose. Katie got plastered and necked like mad with Darren (so much for their fight). I told her it was disgusting, all that slobbering, and she said I was just jealous because I couldn't do the same with Ahmed. I was furious with her. What a cruel thing to say and, really, some friend. I changed seats and sat with Cyn and poured out my heart to her. That was a good idea because Cyn said she had wanted to talk to me since she was going through similar stuff with Yusuf.

"My parents want me to go out with 'a nice Jewish boy,'" she said with a grin, "but I usually date *goyim*. They've disliked most of my boyfriends. It's ironic, but I think Yusuf is the first man they would actually approve of. And he's Muslim!"

I asked her if she and Yusuf ever got physical.

"Sometimes I can tell that he'd let me if I made the first move. But he wouldn't do it himself. We talked about it once. He said he didn't want to 'dishonour' me."

We both shook our heads at that, at the strangeness of it all. Let's face it, that's every Canadian boy's dream—to "dishonour" us as much as possible.

"I'd like to," she admitted, sighing. "I've never felt this strongly about a guy. But I know it wouldn't be good. It would change our relationship. I'd become something that he wouldn't or couldn't love."

I knew exactly what she meant. There are some divides you cannot cross without ruining everything.

It's not really working. I can't think or talk about anything else. I need to nurse this pain. I need to hold it gently against me to try and stop the crying inside.


March 21, 1973

*I* took photos all day today. I couldn't stop. Photographs of Ahmed. The first one was at the gate of Kampung

Pandan, with me. Ray took the picture. Ahmed wore a pale blue summer suit. I was beside him in a blue *baju kurong* and white scarf. He laughed when he saw that we matched.

"We are like twins, Jessie-cah!"

If only, if only. I would gladly be his beloved sister. He stood straight, with his head held high. I looked at the ground. I couldn't face the camera. I was afraid the anguish in my eyes would show.

Then a few pictures of Ahmed and Ray in front of the mosque. When the muezzin cried out the call-to-prayer, Ahmed excused himself and left us. When he came back, he looked refreshed and happy. I took another picture of him then, alone. I imagine his face will be shining with light.

The man in the *restoran* took a pic of the three of us at our table together, lifting glasses of iced tea in a toast. We ordered *mee* soup and curries, but I didn't eat much. The conversation was lively, the three of us talking about Malaysia and Canada, about university, about life.

I didn't take a picture of him at the end of the day, when he left Kampung Pandan. He shook hands with Ray, but not with me of course, and I glanced down so he wouldn't see my misery. That's when he showed me the photograph. It took a while to register what I was looking at. The whole gang was there, all sixty-eight of us, in front of Kampung Pandan with one of the Malaysian youth groups. It was obviously from the first week we had arrived in Malaysia. I grinned to see us looking so white and out of place. Then a cold chill ran up my spine and I stared in shock. There I was with a big stupid smile on my face, getting into the act of being welcomed to Malaysia, and there standing *right beside me* in a white suit and black fez—was Ahmed!

"You mean we actually met back then?!"

I felt sick as I looked at him. Ashamed and heartbroken. He must have been one more Malay face in a sea of Malay faces. Tears pricked the corner of my eyes. I couldn't hide them.

Ahmed smiled sadly and shook his head. I could see tears in his eyes answering mine.

"I, too, do not remember this moment when we stood by each other and no doubt exchanged words. For me, all of you were Canadian youth and I could not tell one from the other. It was only after I worked with the first group in Terengganu that I was able to truly see your people and come to know you. But we should not weep, my sister. Let us be happy, instead, that our eyes were opened."

He gave me the photo. No matter how much I stare at it, I still can't remember meeting him or talking with him that day.

March 22, 1973
*SELAMAT TINGGAL, MALAYSIA, SALAAM ALAYKUM*

*U*p at 6:15 this morning to finish packing the last things, my nightie, slippers and toiletries. Everyone was in a fever of last-minute packing, sitting on bulging suitcases to zip them up, some complaining about things being lost or stolen (it never stops). I made up with Katie last night. She was out drinking with Darren and Jean-François and got totally confused about which one she wanted. Then she said she thought about me and realized what a hard time I was going through. She left the two of them in the bar and came back to find me.

"I'm sorry, Jesse, I really am," she said. "I've been so caught up with my own stuff, I've been a lousy friend."

I accepted her apologies gladly and offered my own. After all I've been as caught up with Ahmed. We had a good long talk, like old times, and swore we'd always be friends.

I'm writing this sitting on my bunk, my suitcases beside me. Katie just came in to say the bus is here. She asked me if I was okay and gave me a hug. Cyn came by earlier to check on me too, but I didn't feel like talking to anyone. Ahmed should be here any minute. He's coming on the bus, as is Yusuf to say goodbye to Cyn, and some friends of the other kids. I'm shaking inside. It's such an effort to keep back all the tears. A reservoir of sadness. I'm not ready for this. I keep thinking that a solution will present itself somehow. Oh God, what can I do?

Later (written on the plane):

He sat beside me on the bus and talked casually about Kuala Lumpur and how it was changing so quickly. I made inane remarks about Canada being a young country too and how it would probably look different when I got back, new things built and so on. His face was stiff. He was clenching his jaw. His eyes showed his anguish and the confusion it caused him. He was in formal Malay dress, all white, with a black fez. The President of the National Federation of Islamic Youth had dressed to honour me. I wore a pink *baju kurong* with red flowers and a green scarf

191

on my head. The other kids gave me odd looks as they were all in Western clothes, on their way home. I ignored them, held my head high. As long as I was with Ahmed, I didn't care. We sat together, like a Malay couple surrounded by foreigners.

At the airport everyone was saying goodbye to various friends, officials, adopted families. But no one really lingered. There was lots of press taking photos. I shied away from the crowd even as Ahmed did. We stood beside each other awkwardly yet determinedly, as if we were going to take every last second we had together regardless of what the world might think, regardless even of our own feelings or thoughts. The stubbornness of love. Soon everyone was boarding the plane and I knew I had to follow them. Then it arrived—like a great soft blow—the final moment of parting. I wasn't prepared at all, though it had been looming over us for weeks. I think I uttered a little cry, like a bird struck down by an arrow, but maybe that was my imagination. I know the sudden jolt of agony hit Ahmed too as I finally looked at him, and reality, squarely in the face, if only to say goodbye.

I could sense the airplane behind me, like a great silver bird from an Arabian tale, waiting to take me away from my beloved prince.

When he spoke, his voice echoed with the tears I could see gathering in his eyes.

"To God we belong and to God we return. That is what a Muslim says, Jessie-cah, when he must accept what is most painful to him. Though we are a great distance apart, our hearts will always be near each other. *Salaam alaykum,* my beloved sister."

I choked out my words.

"I shall always think of you. I shall never forget you. God keep you, Ahmed."

There was nothing left to say. Nothing else we could do. I was about to turn and go when I saw his hands move, a slight flutter like a bird about to rise into the sky. They were cupped towards me and I knew what it meant. His heart lay there and he was offering it to me. I reached out also and I felt the tearing inside, as my heart went with my hands to meet his. The exchange was made. When he withdrew his hands and touched his breast, my heart was placed there, even as his came to me cupped in my palms.

"It's time to go now, Jesse."

I heard Val's voice somewhere behind me, but I couldn't see. I was blinded by tears and light and love and sorrow. I remember stumbling towards the gate and looking back, once, to see Ahmed's face twisted with grief. I clutched at Val, I could barely walk.

They say you can't die of a broken heart, but oh my dear God, I wish I could.

Later again:

I'm looking at the immense blue of the sky, that bright blue country of hope and freedom. It gives me peace despite the pain. Ahmed's heart beats within me. My heart beats elsewhere. This is true, I know, for the rest of my life. There will always be a heart that beats in Malaysia for me. And there will always be a light in Canada that shines towards the East.

# Glossary

*Words and phrases in Bahasa Malaysia
not translated in the book:*

*Saya chakap Bahasa Malaysia sedikit.*
I speak the Malaysian language a little.

*jangan*—do not

*Saya pandai chakap Melayu? Ya! Saya suka Bahasa Malaysia dan
saya harap saya akan chakap dengan banyak orang$_2$—kawan$_2$!—di
Malaysia bila saya tinggal disitu.*
Can I speak Malay? Yes! I like the Malaysian language and I hope
I will speak with many people—friends!—in Malaysia when I
stay there.

A mixed language (French and Malay) sentence:
*Je pense que saya akan jalan sou!*
I think that I will go crazy!
*Mais saya chinta!*
But I love it!

*Tuan tuan dan puan puan dan belia belia Canada.*
Gentlemen and ladies and youth of Canada.

*terimakaseh*—Thank you

*kopi*—coffee
*teh*—tea

*Nama saya…*—My name is…

*Di gigit semut, siapa sakit naik atas.*
Being bitten by an ant, whoever feels the pain goes up.
(Children's game with hands on top of each other's hands. The bottom hand gets pinched like the bite of an ant and goes to the top. You sing the song as you play, going faster and faster.)

*Serjan mejar*—Sergeant major